Secrets of the SKY

Secrets of the SKY

by Guido Ruggieri

translated and adapted by
Deryck D. Bayliss, Ph.D.

PAUL HAMLYN
London · New York · Sydney · Toronto

Photographic Acknowledgements

The letters below indicate the position of photographs as they appear on each page:
T=Top B=Bottom C=Centre L=Left R=Right

Aerofilms Ltd., London: 42*RB*; ANSA: 94; Archivo Mondadori: 81*L*, 114; Archivo Mondadori-EDERA: 24, 52–3, 89, 103, 118–19, 120, 127, 149; Arpac-Mekhetarian, Brussels: 12*TL*; Asiago Observatory: 151*B*; Associated Press: 14–15, 50, 61*TL*; Servizio Baldi: 162; Biblioteca Nazionale Marciana: 121; Walter Bonatti: 25–6, 37*TL*, 87; California Institute of Technology and Carnegie Institution of Washington: 132–3, 136, 150, 151*B*, 154, 155; Conzett and Huber: 27, 38, 39; Mario de Biasi: 22*BR*, 29, 40*T*, 98; Cornelius de Witt: 45*B*; Hans Erni: 42*L*; EST: 16, 30–1, 56–7, 60–1, 66–7, 73, 76, 99, 106*TL*, 109*T*, 111, 129, 130, 133, 137, 145*B*, 146, 147, 164*TR*; Farabola: 63; Giraudon: 43; Kodak-J.T. Williams, Director, Oregon Pass Observatory and Carlos Troncoso Maza: 112–13; Kored Book Ancyc 6/6 Travis-St Mauston: 35; Librairie Larousse, Paris: 65*BR*; Life: 67, 156–7; Lotti: 49; Lowell Observatory: 102; Lund Astronomical Institute: 144, 145; Magnum Photos: 37*R*, 75, 123; T. Maloney: 104; Museo di Storia della Scienza di Firenze: 105*L*; NASA: 19, 21*R* and *L*, 33, 55*T*, 90, 95, 166, 167, 168; Newsweek: 142; Novosti Agency, Moscow: 17*B*; Oriental Institute, University of Chicago, 48; Palais de la Découverte, Paris: 68–9; Rossetti: 142–3; Rudaux and Vaucouleurs: 96; Scientific American: 72, 134–5; SEF, Turin: 27*R*; Ch. Spehner: 34*BR*; Sidney W. Woods: 152, 153, 170; World Book: 61*BL*, 172, 173; Zauli Ferrari: 46.

Opposite the frontispiece: *An old print of the world system, the Sun, the Earth, the planets and the Zodiac (from* Harmonia Macrocosmica *by Andrea Cellarius).*

Published 1969 by
The Hamlyn Publishing Group Limited
London · New York · Sydney · Toronto,
Hamlyn House, Feltham, Middlesex, England
for Golden Pleasure Books Ltd.

Printed in Italy by Officine Grafiche
Arnoldo Mondadori Editore - Verona

CONTENTS

Part One

THE EARTH

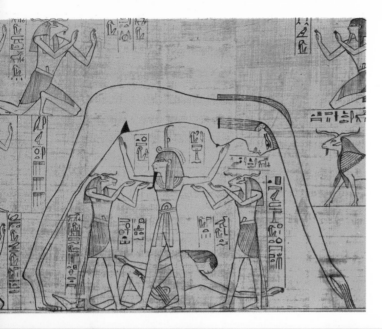

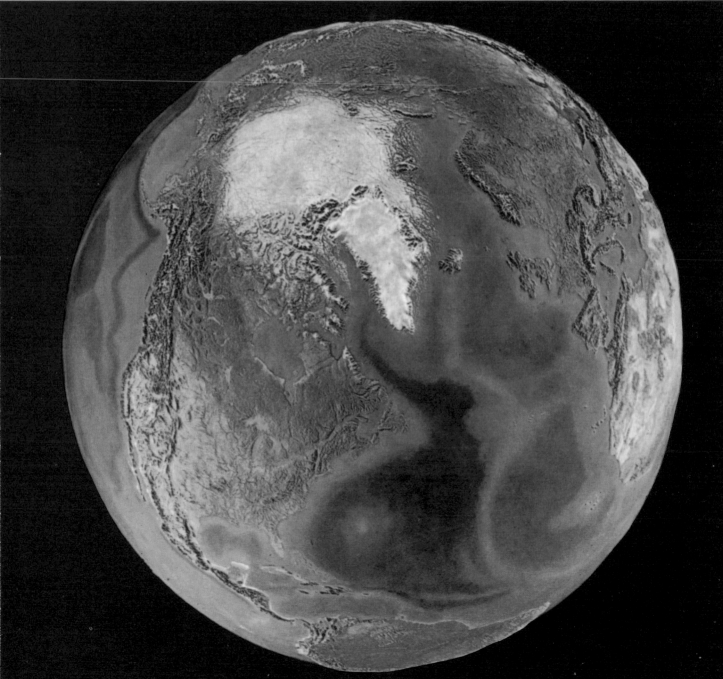

THE SHAPE OF THE EARTH

On 23 August 1966 the space probe *Orbiter 1* transmitted to the Earth photographs of a lunar region scattered with craters. Prominent in the sky, above the desolate surface, was a large planet illuminated by the Sun, similar to the crescent Moon seen after sunset. The planet was the Earth, itself, photographed as it actually appears in space—a globular form suspended as an isolated body in the sky. The planet nearest Earth, Venus, appears in the telescope under the right conditions exactly like our world as seen from *Orbiter*. The Earth is shown to be, therefore, similar to the Moon and also similar to the planets.

Man's physical size in relation to the planet on which he lives impedes his perception of the fact that the huge Earth is an isolated celestial body. As a result, man has many mistaken visual impressions of the Earth. If he is only persuaded by what he can see with the naked eye, then he must believe that he lives on an Earth which extends only as far as the eye can see, even if it is wrinkled in certain parts by the great mountain folds and troughs of the valleys. The human eye sees that above the 'flat' Earth is the sky, which appears to be an azure dome resting a long way away on the horizon. Only after centuries of doubts, hesitations, and increasingly sophisticated astronomical research has man arrived at an understanding of the position in the skies of the planet on which he lives.

Almost five thousand years ago, the great pyramids were raised towards the sky at the edge of the tawny Libyan desert. At that time, the Egyptians thought of the Earth as a plain with the Nile, the river pre-eminent, flowing through its centre. This plain floated on an expanse of water and supported the air on which the vault of the heavens rested. The universe was thus complete. The cosmic elements were deified by the Egyptians; the Earth, Geb, was a great reclining God and Nut was the sky Goddess bent down with her hands and feet resting at the extreme edges of the world. The ancient Babylonians also thought that the flat Earth floated on water, but, in addition, they thought that other waters, distinct from those in the great abyss, existed above the sky which supported them like a solid vault. The Hebrew writers of the Old Testament saw the universe in the same way; and Job spoke of the dense obscurity which surrounded the great ocean which flowed all around the Earth.

Long ago humanity was still childlike; questions were asked of all things visible and imaginary answers were given. The Greeks in Homer's time imagined the ocean in the same way as the Hebrews and the Babylonians had: a belt of water around the known world; but they believed it was a great river in constant motion supplied from inaccessible springs in the far West. They differed from the people in the East, since they did not believe the Earth floated on deep waters. They thought that its round and flat disc was mounted on giant columns whose foundations were lost in the unknown. Atlas guarded these fabulous columns and held up the world on his shoulders. Every day the Sun, personified by the God Phoebus, travelled the vault of the heavens in a flaming chariot which sank in the evening into the waves of the ocean. In the mornings, the chariot and the God emerged after a

Top left: *The universe as symbolised on an ancient Egyptian papyrus: Nut, the Goddess of of the Sky, rests on the Earth which is sustained by Shu, the God of the Air, behind whom is the Lord of the Earth, Geb.*

Top right: *The Earth, as imagined by the Greeks at the time of Homer, was round, flat and encircled by the insuperable 'Ocean River'.*

Left below: *The Earth is a sphere isolated in space.*

subterranean journey on a golden ship, the mysterious work of Vulcan. The Greeks saw in the present Straits of Gibraltar the limit of the known world; they thought that Hercules had separated the two opposing promontories, opening a door to mystery which no one should pass through because beyond lay chaos.

The Greeks sought to give a representative idea of the dimensions of this universe without clearly defining its limits. At the time of the poet Hesiod (flourishing c. 735 B.C.) it was thought that an avil falling from the starry vault of the sky would take nine days and nine nights to reach the Earth, and as much time again to arrive at the base of the columns which supported it from eternity. Today this idea makes us smile. It has been calculated that a ray of light would take four seconds to traverse the whole journey of the legendary anvil. This time is short, indeed, when compared with the thousands of millions of light years which modern astronomers speak of when describing the universe.

The world expanded steadily with the exploration of the daring Phoenicians who passed through the columns of Hercules and discovered new shores. The Earth's foundations, reputedly constructed by the Gods to support the great blue vault of the sky, receded into the distance. Doubt was sown that such foundations even existed and over the centuries the idea of a spherical Earth slowly emerged to override the old concept of the great disc, the weight of which destiny had placed on Atlas's shoulders.

Journeys into various parts of the known world had shown that shadows cast by objects where shorter in North Africa than in Attica or Peloponnesos, which indicated that the Sun illuminated a spherical surface not a flat one. Moreover, the elementary proof of the Earth's spherical shape had been discovered from the way in which ships disappeared over the horizon when they sailed away. From this evidence, Greek thinkers drew the first deductions about the true shape of our world, and slowly a more realistic view of the Earth emerged.

Briefly, simple proof of the spherical shape of the Earth can be obtained by standing on the sea-shore and watching the movement of a ship. If the surface of the sea were perfectly flat, a ship moving into the distance would become gradually smaller and smaller and finally disappear. But, on the contrary, first the hull of the ship disappears from view, and then the superstructure, because it is sailing on a curved surface. With a good pair of prismatic binoculars, the sight is quite disconcerting: it seems that when the hull has disappeared over the horizon, the boat is hidden by a rippling wall of waves above which appear the tops of its masts.

To persuade ourselves that the part of the sea between us and the vanishing ship is part of a sphere is difficult because the illusion of the Earth being flat is so strong. Only if we are projected into space does this optical illusion disappear. When boosted six han-

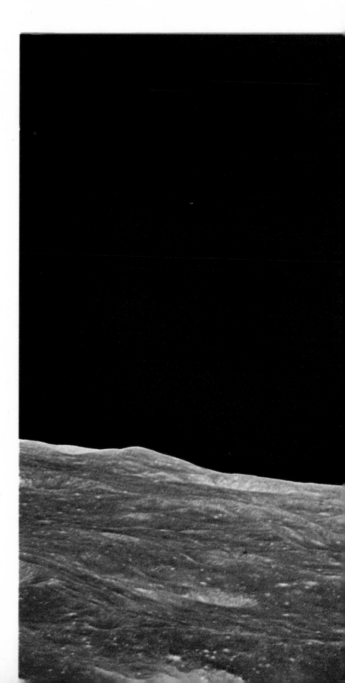

dred miles or more into space, astronauts have clearly seen the curved horizon which so perfectly outlines the spherical shape of our planet.

Because we live in an exciting era of journeys into space, it is easy for us to accept the fact that the Earth is a globe. But it was extremely difficult for people in ancient times to conquer their illusion of the flatness of the Earth. Man only discovered very slowly the true shape of his planet; for many centuries he was influenced by inaccurate religious and scientific beliefs.

Nevertheless, in the sixth century B.C., a group of philosophers did teach that the Earth was a globe (the concept of a spherical Earth). Just three hundred years later, Eratosthenes of Alexandria, a scientific

Right: *An old engraving of Atlas, the mythical giant who, having aided the Titans, was condemned by Jupiter to support the world on his shoulders.*

Below: *This famous photograph of the Earth was taken from* Apollo 8 *in orbit around the Moon at Christmas, 1968. The surface of the Moon can be seen in the foreground.*

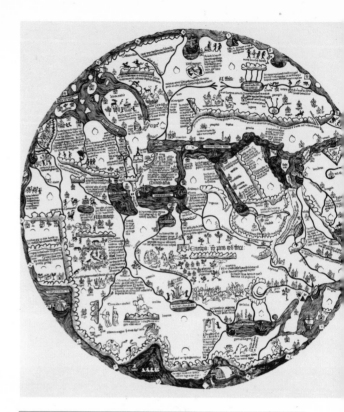

writer (*c.* 276 – *c.* 194 B.C.), calculated—although only roughly—the dimensions of Earth. His calculations revealed for the first time the enormous size and the correct geometrical shape of the planet on which we live.

When the Solar System is discussed in Part Three of this book (See page 77), we shall see how the Greeks viewed the universe after they had established that the Earth was round and isolated in space. For the moment, however, it is interesting to note the great step forward they made. After Eratosthenes, they no longer believed in the springs of the Ocean River or the existence of caves buried deep in the Earth where the Sun God travelled during the night.

Although it seems strange, those early beliefs about the Earth reappeared later, even though changed in form. After the fall of Greek science and the dispersal of the great Greek manuscripts and volumes when the ancient library of Alexandria was destroyed, almost all that had been discovered was forgotten, and the idea of a flat Earth was reborn. At the beginning of the modern era (about the fifth century A.D.), scholars prepared strange maps of the universe (called cosmographies) in which the Earth was sometimes described as a disc and sometimes as a plane with straight sides. Cosmas

of Alexandria (sixth century A.D.) showed the Earth as a rectangular plane surrounded on all sides by huge solid walls which formed arches high in the celestial vault; above the vault were the waters of the heavens—a concept similar to that held by the Babylonians two thousand years before. Later, when the idea of the curvature of the terrestrial surface was accepted, even stranger conclusions were drawn. The Arab geographer Idrisi (twelfth century) imagined the Earth in the shape of an egg floating on an hypothetical ocean: the egg floated vertically upon the deep waters and the inhabited world was perched on the top.

But at last the concept of a spherical and isolated Earth reappeared. The Italian poet Dante Alighieri (1265–1321) described it thus in the *Divine Comedy* and so did the geographers and cosmographers when they

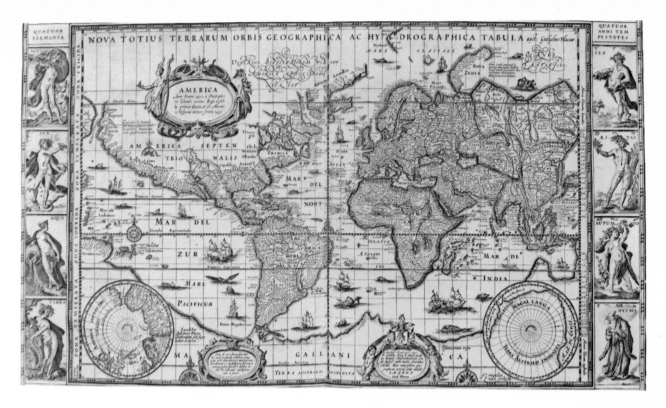

NOVA TOTIUS TERRARUM ORBIS GEOGRAPHICA AC HYDROGRAPHICA TABULA

Above: *A seventeenth century* A.D. *map of the world after Christopher Columbus' voyages of exploration had confirmed that the Earth was a sphere.*

Below: *The control panel of the Russian space ship* Vostok; *the terrestrial globe appears among the other navigational instruments.*

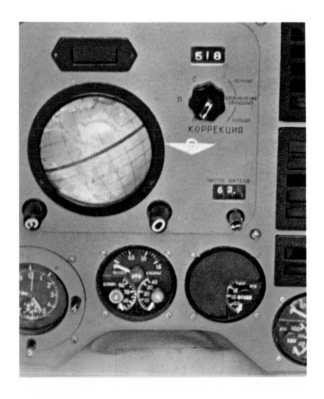

collected the reports brought back by adventurous explorers and navigators from distant regions. With the voyages of Christopher Columbus in the fifteenth century, people at last had to accept the Earth's form as it really was and not as they imagined it or wanted it to be.

Columbus, Amerigo Vespucci and Ferdinand Magellan slowly followed the curvature of the globe, blown by the ocean winds which filled the great sails of their ships. Today, in the space capsules orbiting outside the Earth's atmosphere, other men journey rapidly above the continents and oceans and see below them the perfect arc of the terrestrial surface. In front of the exploring astronauts, on the control panel of each space capsule, there is a small globe which stands out among the complicated instruments: it is a representation of the Earth and it slowly rotates under the astronauts' eyes showing the areas over which they are passing. This sphere, which is an exact representation of our planet, replaces the navigation maps which early explorers used.

Today there is no longer any doubt about the shape of the Earth and its dimensions, although scientists and astronomers are continually expanding their knowledge of the Earth's position in relation to the universe.

THE EARTH AND ITS ATMOSPHERE

How Big is the Earth?

The great difference in size between man and the Earth he inhabits has been discussed, but the relationship has not been precisely defined. Just what is man's real size in relation to the planet on which he builds cities and on which he passes his life? This question introduces the subject of the Earth's size and dimensions.

Man is often compared in size to the terrestrial sphere as ants are to an orange or an apple. The proportions are not exact, of course, but the comparison is used because it gives a representative idea of the relative size. However, if the ratio between the ant and the apple to man and the Earth is carried out in correct mathematical proportions, man would be six hundred miles tall, or two hundred and ten times higher than Mont Blanc in the Alps. On the other hand, if we could reduce our planet to the size of an apple, then man would assume the dimensions of a molecule and his biggest cities—London, Paris, New York or Tokyo—would be about as large as certain tiny micro-organisms which can only be observed with a powerful microscope.

Comparisons involving the size of the Earth can be made more accurately and easily by using actual figures. The diameter of the Earth at the equator is 12,757 kilometres (7,927 miles). The circumference of the Earth at the equator is 40,077 kilometres (24,902 miles). The diameter measured from the North Pole to the South Pole is different, because our globe is not a perfect sphere but is slightly flattened at the poles. This second diameter is 12,714 kilometres (7,900 miles). The polar flattening is the result of the Earth's rotational movements which have increased the equatorial diameter as a result of centrifugal forces. The difference between the two diameters is, however, very small. With the enormous dimensions we have recorded, a difference of 43 kilometres (27 miles) is practically insignificant.

Today's rapid travel in jets suggests that the world is small. But the measurements of the highest mountains and the deepest abysses of the oceans readily demonstrate that modern travel gives a false impression of the Earth's size. If we wish to make a model of the Earth with a diameter of one metre (about three feet), to represent Mt. Everest, the highest mountain (height: 8,848 metres or 29,493 feet), we must make it seven-tenths of a millimetre in height. To reproduce to scale the greatest ocean deep, the Marianas Trench, which is 10,915 metres (36,383 feet) below sea level according to the latest soundings, we must make a depression one and two-tenths of a millimetre deep. In September 1966, the American astronauts Richard Gordon and Charles Conrad, in the space capsule *Gemini 11*, saw India 600 miles below them and could discern the Himalaya Mountains on the horizon as a white line under the bright clouds. The world's highest mountain chain did not even seem to touch the black sky above the gentle curvature of the Earth; and yet in that apparently flat area were hidden colossal rocks, terrifying ice slopes several thousand feet high and valleys so deep that it would take several weeks of hazardous climbing to descend to their floors.

The Atmosphere

At this point we have acquired a realistic idea of the Earth's size and of its isolation in space. Surrounding the Earth is the sky which is as much part of the Earth as the rocks of its crust; this is the transparent atmosphere through which light from distant worlds reaches us. When the surface of our globe is spread out below the space capsules

Opposite: *India photographed from the space capsule* Gemini 11, *1000 kilometres (620 miles) above the Earth. The curvature of the horizon just cuts across the great Himalayan mountain chain, seen as a white area in the distance.*

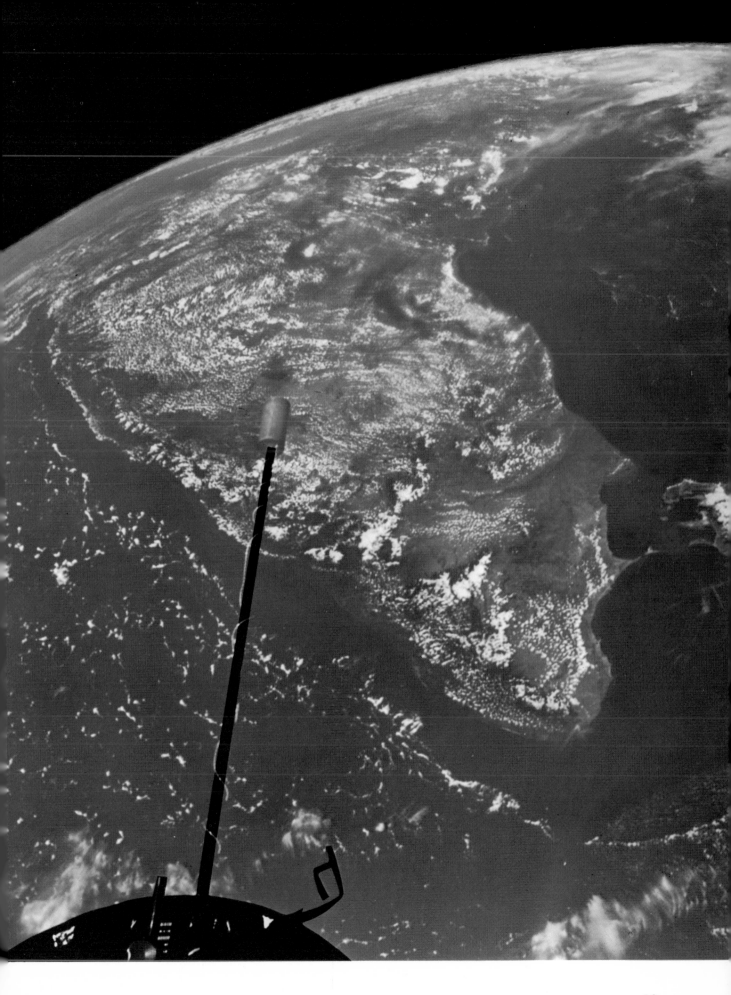

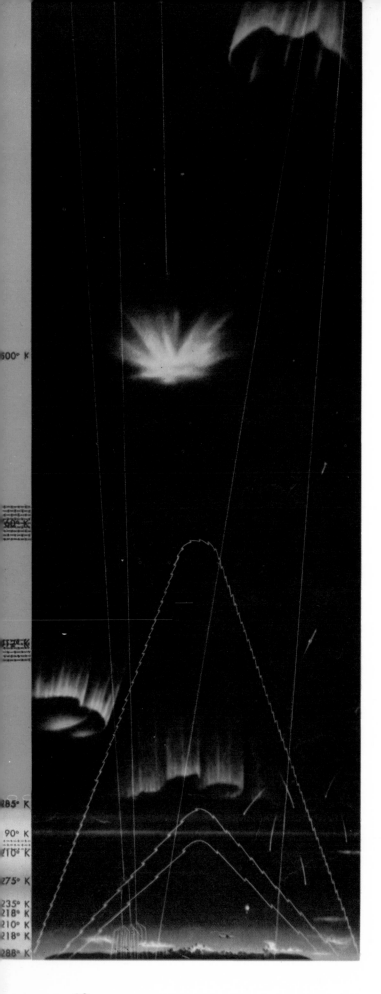

600° K

300° K

285° K

90° K
210° K
275° K

235° K
218° K
210° K
218° K

288° K

orbiting from a height of hundreds of miles, a stupendous view of light and colour is revealed to the astronauts. There is an alternation of colours from the indigo blue of the oceans to the dark emerald of the tropical forests; through the overlying clouds the ochre of the deserts can be seen full of unexpected hues, even intense orange and blazing red. Above this spectacular sight the familiar blue of the sky which we see from the Earth's surface is completely lacking. In spite of a space capsule being bathed in brilliant sunshine, the astronauts can see the stars in the black sky as well as the Moon shining as brightly as on the darkest night. This is because astronauts navigate beyond the atmosphere and, therefore, do not see the optical effects it creates of a luminous vault which may rise above our horizons, red at dawn, dark blue at sunset. If, for some unforeseen reason, the atmosphere suddenly disappeared we would find that the Earth seemed to be occupying empty space. The sky would be uniformly black, the sound of the wind would disappear, and no clouds would pass over our heads. The most distant mountains, which are shrouded in a delicate blue haze and wreathed with clouds, would

stand out on the horizon outlined in stark light and shade. The terrestrial landscape would assume the appearance of that of the Moon and every living thing would be destroyed. The Earth would become a dead planet like the Moon and like other satellites and desolate worlds in space.

The atmosphere surrounding Earth gives us life, as well as the colours of our sky. We live at the bottom of an ocean of air like deep sea fish which move in the hidden recesses of the oceans. The deep sea fish do not notice the pressure to which they are subjected because it is equally distributed throughout their bodies and all their tissues. We do not notice the pressure of the atmospheric ocean in which we move for the same reason, yet this pressure, for all its apparent weightlessness, is considerable: the atmosphere exerts a pressure of one kilogram on every square centimetre ($14\frac{1}{2}$ lb per square inch) of the Earth's surface. Because our bodies are perfectly conditioned to the environment in which we are born, we must equip our high flying aeroplanes with air-tight compartments for flights where the air is thin. And we must also take care that sufficient oxygen reaches our lungs because respiration is very

difficult or impossible in rarefied air. Like the creatures that live in the profound abyss of the sea, we are made to remain on the floor of our ocean; only with sufficient protection from loss of atmospheric pressure can man rise above the Earth's atmosphere into outer space.

The Layers of the Atmosphere

The blue vault of air, where the clouds sail and where the rainbows arch, is a mixture of gas held around the Earth by the force of gravity. This gas exists in a state of minute particles and is present as layers which decrease in density upwards because the force of gravity slowly diminishes with increasing distance from the Earth's surface. The atoms and molecules in the atmosphere move continuously in all directions and it is inevitable that some of these succeed in escaping into space. However, the gravitational attraction of our planet is a strong brake on this turbulent atmospheric ocean. Only if the Earth's gravity were reduced to a very low level would its atmosphere expand and disperse. Celestial bodies with weak gravitational forces cannot possibly maintain their atmospheric covering as the Earth

Above: *Mist and clouds form in the troposphere. Here is a fine picture of cumulous clouds.*
Below left: *Microscopic crystals of ice are formed when water vapour is frozen.*
Below right: *Water vapour freezing on the trees in winter clothes them with a fairy tale embroidery.*

does and they are exposed to the intense heat and cold of space, after a certain period of time. The varied conditions found on other worlds is, therefore, partially explained by the amount of gravitational attraction which they exert.

At sea level the air is composed of three-quarters nitrogen and the remainder oxygen with traces of carbon dioxide and other so-called rare gases. Water is also permanently present in the atmosphere as vapour. Reduction in temperature causes the water to condense and thus form mists, clouds, beautiful tiny crystals of ice which comprise snow-flakes, humid curtains of dew and the frozen, crystalline winter clothing of the trees. Finally, there are minute solid particles in the air which constitute the fine dust of the atmosphere. We are aware of the presence of these particles as dust when the Sun's rays filter through the clouds or through the branches of trees.

Nine-tenths of the gas in the atmosphere exists at its lowest level, the troposphere, which extends from sea level to a height of about 12 kilometres ($7\frac{1}{2}$ miles). In this layer clouds, thunderstorms and cyclones are formed. The meteorological conditions which govern fine weather and rain are exclusive to the troposphere, so in a strict sense it can be called the atmosphere even though we cannot reach its top in aircraft without pressurised cabins. In this layer of the atmosphere the density diminishes rapidly towards the top, and the temperature decreases so that above the equator we find at the outer limit of the tropospheric layer a temperature which is —55° C. (or —72° F.).

The tropopause, which is a narrow zone above the blue troposphere, is traversed by immensely violent winds. Above this begins the stratosphere where the air is much calmer and extremely thin; it extends to a height of more or less 80 kilometres (50 miles) above the Earth's surface. In the stratosphere, which is the beginning of the upper atmosphere of the Earth, the air is so thin that it contains practically no water vapour at all. As a result, there is no moisture, rain or snow in this layer.

The shell of air which covers the Earth continues still higher but is incredibly thin or rarefied. Above the limit of the stratosphere, the stratopause and the ionosphere extend into the dark sky, a million times more rarefied than the air we breathe. Although the atmosphere is very thin, the gas particles of the ionosphere absorb the greater part of the radiation dangerous to life on Earth and cause the disintegration of all but the smallest meteors. Together with the stratosphere, which contains ozone, a power-ful filter for the ultra-violet rays of the Sun, this great envelope of the ionosphere, made almost of nothing apart from gas molecules, enables life to flourish on Earth.

In the ionosphere there are very high temperatures. At a height of 250 kilometres (155 miles) it is 650° C. (1,200° F.) and even greater at higher altitudes, but this heat is distributed amongst the gas molecules which are widely separated. The interval between molecules in the ionosphere is so great that it is not possible to notice any material present there. The astronauts who have passed through the ionosphere have seen the Earth, with its denser enveloping atmosphere, separated from them exactly as if they were looking at it from the emptiness of space.

Yet still higher there is another layer with definite physical characteristics. This is the exosphere which is incredibly tenuous, or thin, and incredibly hot. It is necessary to go up to a height of 2,400 kilometres (1,491 miles) above the Earth's surface in order to reach interplanetary space, in the narrowest sense of the word, where there are few dispersed molecules.

In the last two atmospheric layers from 80 to 800–1,000 kilometres high (50 to 500–625 miles) the polar auroras blaze in all their splendours. These phenomena are governed by solar radiation and are concentrated around the magnetic poles of the Earth and, therefore, are close to the geographical poles. The Aurora Borealis shines over the North Pole and the Aurora Australis over the South Pole; the auroras are sometimes called the 'northern lights' and the 'southern lights'. Occasionally the auroral phenomenon is particularly intense and the lights are visible as far away as the temperate zones or even in the tropics.

THE COLOURS IN A RAY OF SUNSHINE

For those who are fascinated by colour, a cut glass vase or a crystal chandelier is particularly impressive. When the vase or chandelier is illuminated, rays of coloured light burst from the dazzling glass faces or pendants and the colours change with the slightest movement of either the object or the person observing. These glass faces and pendants display a phenomenon which provides a key to an understanding of the colours of the sky: light breaks up or divides into various colours.

The small chandeliers and lamps made by man cannot compare with the nearest lamp in the Milky Way galaxy—the Sun. If a thin beam of its light enters a dark room and is directed on to a white screen, and if a glass prism is placed in the path of the beam, the spot of white light which first appeared on the screen is replaced by a strip of light which contains the colours of the rainbow. This strip of light is called a *spectrum*. Although it is impossible to distinguish all the tints and hues in a spectrum, there are seven fundamental colours which are readily visible: red, orange, yellow, green, blue, indigo and violet, in that order.

The great British scientist, Sir Isaac Newton, made the first steps towards the discovery of the composition of light. It was Newton who first passed a ray of sunlight through a glass prism, proving that white light could be separated into individual coloured components—the visible spectrum.

What happens when a ray of sunlight strikes a prism? The hidden colours in the ray are refracted, or bent, as they pass from one medium to another, and are separated according to their wavelengths as they pass through the surfaces of the prism. The bending of the ray of white light into colours reveals the true composition of sunlight.

The light waves which reach us from the Sun are of different wavelengths; for example, at one end of the spectrum, red light travels on a wavelength of 631 millionths of a millimetre, while at the other end violet light travels on a shorter wave length of 430 millionths of a millimetre. All the other colours have intermediate wavelengths. The human eye sees the colours fused together as white light, but in passing through the prism the shortest light waves are refracted more than the longest waves and thus the beam of white light is bent open like a fan and becomes a slice of a rainbow.

In the atmosphere the light waves behave differently according to their various wavelengths. As they strike the molecules of gas which compose the air, parts of the waves are dispersed; the dispersion is greatest for the short waves. The diffused light which results colours the sky blue. If there were no atmosphere the sky would be black because there would not be any dispersion of light waves.

Below and right: *After passing through a glass prism, a ray of sunlight is broken up into the colours of the rainbow.*
Far right: *The sun is low and only red rays filter through the atmosphere.*

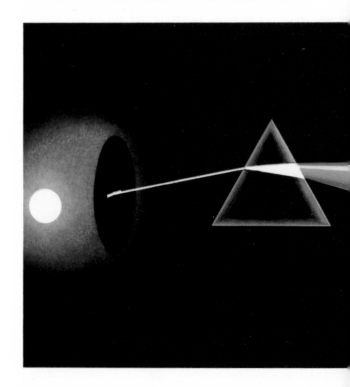

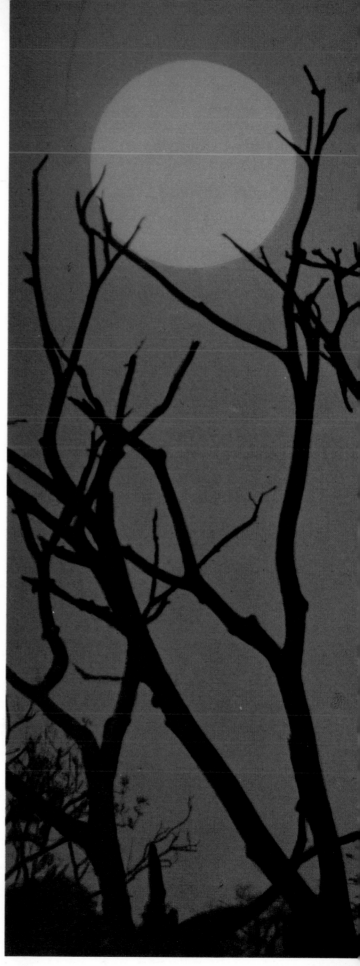

The absence of atmosphere is the reason why the astronauts saw a brilliant Sun shining in a black sky and why in high mountains where the molecules of air are much rarer than in the plains the sky is dark and the blue assumes a shade which approaches indigo. Naturally, during the night no external light brightens the atmosphere and there is no dispersion even at the Earth's surface: the blue sky appears black and the stars, which are hidden during the day, appear.

When the Sun is near the horizon at sunset or sunrise its rays are filtered by the thick atmosphere through which they must pass. The short waves no longer reach our eyes; we therefore see the Sun through the long waves which reach us and its disc assumes the colours of flames. The clouds around the Sun, or the fine dust suspended in the atmosphere, are coloured pink or red as well, and the sky blazes with colour. If the horizon is free from mists, as often happens in the mountains, the red light of the Sun brightly illuminates the landscape and everything changes its usual appearance, becoming suffused with warm reddish or purplish tints.

The atmosphere is not limited to diffusing or filtering the colours hidden in the Sun's rays; it can create the appearance of the solar spectrum, when there are crystals of ice suspended in it which act like miniature prisms. The so-called 'haloes' are formed in this way; they are great circles or bands around the Sun or the Moon composed of more or less intense iridescent colours. Even more effective than crystals are droplets of water in the atmosphere which function as prisms when the Sun's rays strike them at a certain angle, forming the rainbow which arches across the sky. This phenomenon appears near the end of rain storms. The marvellous display of a rainbow is composed of pure light in which the seven fundamental colours seem to pulsate because they are so vivid; it is much more imposing than the haloes which generally have pale colours. Often a second is produced by the double reflection of light in the water droplets.

Opposite page: *Photograph of the Dolomites, mountains in the Southern Tyrolese Alps. Under the darkening evening sky, the Moon already shines and the limestone walls are aflame with the last rays of the Sun.*

Below: *The separation of the Sun's light into its constituent colours by the prismatic effect of water droplets creates the marvellous rainbow bridge which sweeps across the sky, presenting a fascinating spectacle.*

DAY AND NIGHT: TIME

The Earth's Rotation

Every day the Sun rises in the east, crosses the sky and sets in the west, and every night the heavens unfold after the light of day is extinguished. The universe appears to turn around us continually, completing one revolution every twenty-four hours; in reality, it is the rotation of the Earth which makes the cosmos seem to be a hollow, moving sphere in which we occupy the centre. This is an illusion which ancient man meditated on for many centuries. Today it is easy to overcome the illusion of the sky circling around the Earth. We can see with a telescope the rotation of other planets, the celestial bodies similar to the Earth. The effects of terrestrial rotation are also obvious in the deviation of the winds which turn in vortices (always in the same direction), in the movement of marine currents and in the polar flattening of our globe.

The perpetual rotation of the Earth is effected in a very regular manner and involves everything, from stable mountains to lightest clouds, from great oceans to drops of rain. No 'wind' is created by this movement; the atmosphere is attached to the Earth like the shell of a nut and follows it completely. Human beings, therefore, cannot appreciate the movement which carries the Earth continuously towards the east except by observing the stars and the entire sky which move perpetually in the opposite direction to the motion of the Earth.

The axis of rotation of our globe passes through the two poles. For the inhabitants of the northern hemisphere, the imaginary prolongation of the axis into the celestial vault almost coincides with the well-known Pole Star, which indicated the north to sailors long ago. In the southern hemisphere the prolongation does not point to any important star, and is some distance from the famous Southern Cross, which navigators in the fifteenth and sixteenth centuries saw rising in the southern skies. Of course, pivots of our axis in the starry sky do not exist, nor is the axis a tangible thing. A simple example of the Earth rotating on its axis would be a billiard ball rotating as a result of being hit laterally without any pivot to sustain it. The twenty-four hours which

Left: *Ancient people believed that the Sun, God of light, travelled across the sky in a golden chariot drawn by four winged horses. At dawn, the reappearance of this fabulous chariot brought day to the Earth again.*

Opposite: *The apparent movement of the Sun is produced by the rotation of the Earth. When the Sun disappears in the west, it is the Earth's rotational movement which carries us into the night.*

extend from one midday to another—the time between moments in which the Sun reaches the maximum height above the horizon—encompass the rotation of the globe. Since the Earth only receives its light on one half at a time the rotational movement around the pole at the axis makes us move towards the Sun in the morning, and towards darkness in the evening. When our position is directly opposite the one we occupied at midday we are at midnight and in the most distant position from the illuminated face of our planet. This is a natural alternation which applies all over the world. As a result of the Earth's globular shape, there is a different time on each meridian or on each arc of the great circles which run through the poles. Every slight movement towards the east or the west should mean an adjustment of our clocks, but in practice the keeping of time is made easier. By international agreement the Earth has been divided into twenty-four segments (or zones) along the meridians; in each zone time is the same. This is the system of the 'time zones' which involve simple adjustments of one hour, either faster or slower, when we pass from one zone to another.

According to this system the zero meridian passes through Greenwich in England. When it is twelve o'clock at Greenwich it is one o'clock in Italy, Germany and in Scandinavia and eleven o'clock in Iceland and on part of the Atlantic Ocean. At the same moment in New York it is seven in the morning, while in San Francisco it is four o'clock and still night. In eastern Asia it is already evening and in the zone which includes Japan it is nine o'clock in the evening.

Measurement of Time

Without vibration or sudden movement the planet Earth carries us from daylight to darkness and gives a rhythm to our lives. It is the rotation of the Earth which enables us to measure the passage of time; and it is therefore a gigantic clock on which all clocks made by man are regulated. From the most ancient times man has sought to understand the secret of this great clock. When the measurement of time was invented, it was vague; then slowly, telling time became more accurate, and eventually became advanced to the precision of today.

Long ago man read the time from a natural quadrant (a Sun-dial) based on the length of shadows cast by the Sun—short at midday, very long in the morning and evenings. In early times the Roman naturalist Pliny (A.D. 23–79), when inviting a friend to his house, wrote to ask him to arrive 'when his shadow was six feet long'. In that case man himself served as the hands of the clock. In ancient Rome, a suitable column was erected to give the time by the length of its shadow to the public. When there was no Sun, or to indicate short periods of time, the hour glass—in which water or fine sand indicated the time while falling from one container into another beneath until it was full—was used. Even ropes with knots tied at regular intervals served as clocks: the ropes were set on fire and time could be told by how many knots were left. Candles with different colour bands were burned and when the colour bands were consumed one could count the passage of regular intervals of time.

Solar clocks, or Sun-dials, have continued in use to the present day; we can still see excellent examples, often artistically decorated, on the front of ancient continental villas; modern Sun-dials are manufactured for display in gardens.

Eventually true clocks with faces and hands were invented and gradually perfected. In A.D. 996 the first great clock, using wheels and driven by a weight, was constructed by a Frenchman, the priest Gerberto, who became Pope Silvester II. In 1511, a Nuremberg craftsman, Peter Henlein, made the first portable clock. In 1657, Christian Huygens (1629–95), a Dutchman, applied the pendulum to huge clocks, following the criteria suggested by Galileo Galilei. These are some of the fundamental steps in the measurement of time which were taken by men in the past.

Today we can read even fractions of a second with small flat wrist watches.

Different Kinds of Time

Of course, the actual keeping of time is more complicated than it appears to the

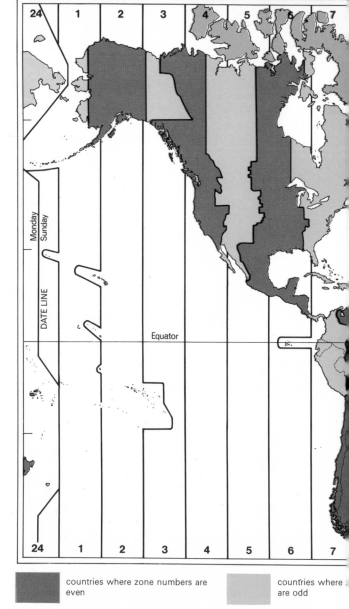

Numbers indicate the hours of the days throughout the

countries where zone numbers are even

countries where are odd

average layman. And, there are several different kind of times. *Sidereal Time*, which is also called 'Star Time', is based upon the actual rotation of the Earth in relation to the point in the starry heavens called the spring, or vernal, equinox. This is a point when the Sun is in the constellation of Pisces (the Fishes), and the spring equinox occurs on March 21st when day and night are of equal length.

Everyday time is based on *Mean Solar Time,* our *Standard time,* in which astonomers have averaged out the *Apparent Solar Time,* which is the time as it is recorded by a Sun-dial.

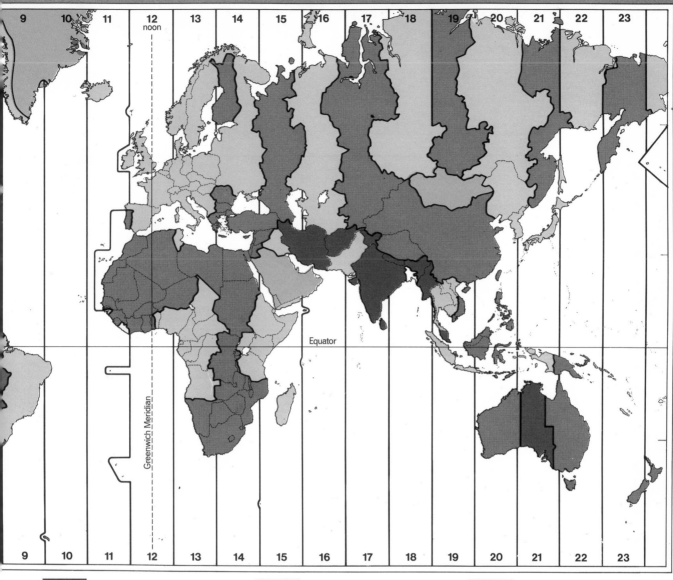

9 10 11 12 noon 13 14 15 16 17 18 19 20 21 22 23

Equator

Greenwich Meridian

9 10 11 12 13 14 15 16 17 18 19 20 21 22 23

rs | countries where the time differs half an hour from neighbouring zones | countries that have not yet adopted the zone system | areas where no regular time is kept

Above: *The time zones. This map illustrates the zones or segments into which the Earth has been divided. In each segment all localities have the same time. For practical reasons the subdivisions do not always follow the meridians exactly, but often follow geographical boundaries. There are also countries which have legal time which differs from that of the zone in which they are actually located.*

Right: *An ancient sand clock, the hour-glass.*

31

UNIVERSAL GRAVITATION

The Centre of Gravity

The Earth has two main movements: first, the rotation about its axis, which results in the Sun and the stars alternating above our horizons. The second movement is the Earth's revolution around the Sun, which explains the annual rhythm of the seasons. To understand how the Earth moves around the Sun, it is necessary to understand that the force of gravity propels our globe through space. Gravity holds all objects to the Earth's surface and compels them to fall towards its centre.

Since the Earth is a sphere, 'up' and 'down' are only relative terms. In Europe and in North America 'down' is below our feet and 'up' is in the sky. But this is equally true for people in Australia and New Zealand, on the other side of the globe, although their feet are opposite to ours and their 'up' is a prolongation of our 'down'. All around the Earth there is no difference in the way abandoned objects fall; and a plumb line always hangs vertically. 'Down' is, therefore, the centre of the planet and 'up' is in the sky whatever place one finds oneself. Dante wrote that the centre of the Earth 'is the point to which weights from all parts are drawn'.

In ancient times the existence of the antipodes (places opposite to each other) was a great obstacle to the concept of a spherical Earth. When the known world was limited by the columns of Hercules, men asked: if the Earth is really a globe, what would happen if we follow its curvature? It was natural to fear that men and animals descending the curved surface would start to slide until they fell off the Earth into space. Men thought, too, that nothing could live on the globe's other side without falling off. After the globe had been circumnavigated, the idea that the centre of the Earth was the centre of gravity was confirmed.

The force with which the Earth attracts objects determines their weights. In times past, the way in which the force of gravity works was wrongly interpreted; it was thought that heavy bodies fell more rapidly than light ones. Galileo was the first to demonstrate that gravity gives to all bodies the same velocity of fall, at the moment they are dropped or abandoned, but that the velocity increases as the bodies continue to fall. Thus, a feather and a piece of lead fall with the same velocity; but this can happen only if the resistance of air is totally eliminated. This experiment is easily performed in a physics laboratory by placing a piece of lead and a feather in a glass tube in which a vacuum has been created; it is always rather surprising to see the two falling objects arrive at the bottom of the tube at the same instant.

The Laws of Gravity

In 1687, a century after Galileo's experiments, Sir Isaac Newton defined the laws of gravity and extended their application to the entire universe. He demonstrated that gravitational attraction exists wherever material bodies are found, large or small; and this explains the movements of the stars and all other bodies in the universe.

The attraction exerted by bodies is proportional to their masses (the amount of material they contain). If two bodies of unequal mass are situated in space they attract each other, and the body with a smaller mass will finally fall on to the body of larger mass. For this reason a large meteor of small mass relative to the Earth falls on to the Earth's surface without its feeble attraction even slightly affecting our planet's position in space.

If we think of the disproportion of mass between our globe and the objects on its surface we can understand how the Earth's gravitational force was once considered to be peculiar to the Earth.

A second extremely important point about gravity is that the force with which two bodies are attracted to one another rapidly diminishes with the increase in their distance from each other. Therefore, if we rise any distance above the Earth's surface, gravity has less effect on us; and this affects our weight which becomes less. As the distance of an object from the Earth increases, its weight naturally decreases until it tends to become negligible, though it never attains a state of absolute weightlessness. An object which moves away from Earth, in every case, eventually reaches a zone in space in which the terrestrial attraction is replaced by that of another planet or another star; therefore, at this point in space, its weight starts to increase again. In the section on the vertical composition of the atmosphere (*See* p. 21), the effect of the decrease of the force of gravity on the layers of air was discussed.

Planetary Motion

At this point one may well wonder what actually happens when gravitational attraction affects a body, which is endowed with its own motion, completely outside the atmosphere. Take, as a straightforward example, a meteor. Without the resistance of the air, the only force that can make a meteor deviate from its usual path and so fall on the Earth is the force of gravity. An interesting point, however, is that if the force which impelled the object were even greater than the gravitational attraction the meteor would inevitably continue in its flight, although finding itself subjected to a

A photograph of the American astronaut Edward H. White 'walking in space', taken from **Gemini** 4.

Above left: *A sixteenth century print of the Danish astronomer Tycho Brahe (1546-1630).*

Top right: *Galileo Galilei (1564-1642) who founded the field of experimental science.*

Centre right: *Isaac Newton (1643-1727) who discovered the laws of universal gravitation.*

Bottom right: *Johann Kepler (1571-1630) who discovered the laws which govern the orbital motions of celestial bodies.*

more or less pronounced deviation in its path.

A still more fascinating case could conceivably occur if the deviation towards the Earth and the consequent increase in velocity undergone by the meteor placed it in a condition of equilibrium, due to the tendency to fly off into space being nullified by gravitational attraction. The result would be that the meteor would neither be capable of falling or shooting into space; it would be chained by the equilibrium of forces and would have no option but to move around the Earth. That is to say, the meteor would be placed in orbit.

There is an extremely simple and effective way of grasping what would happen under these circumstances. By tying a cord firmly round a stone and swinging it round and round with a slow circular motion, one will immediately see that the tendency is for the stone to fly outwards as a result of centrifugal force, and it is only the cord that prevents it escaping. The hand which holds the cord is acting, therefore, as the Earth, and the stone as the meteor. The cord, of course, represents the force of gravity which, in reality, has no material appearance, but which is a great deal stronger than any bond man could ever construct. When it is a question of artificial satellites revolving around the Earth, and the planets revolving around the Sun, the principle involved is exactly the same.

A body gravitating around another does not describe a perfect circle but an ellipse, a geometrical figure which is more or less a flattened circle. All the planets move in elliptical orbits; therefore, their distances from the Sun vary continually, from a minimum, the *perihelion*, to a maximum, the *aphelion*. The word *perihelion* actually means 'nearest the Sun' and it comes from two Greek words *peri* = near and *helios* = Sun. On the other hand, *aphelion* actually means 'far from the Sun' and comes from the Greek word *apo* = off and *helios*. In the case of a satellite orbiting the Earth, these particular points are referred to by the names perigee and apogee. The discovery that orbits are elliptical was made by the great German astronomer and mathematician Johann Kepler who in the early years of the seventeenth century calculated and eventually established the laws of planetary movements.

These laws, however, were a mystery until universal gravitation was defined by Sir Isaac Newton. Newton's laws of gravitation explained and summarised the planetary movements and stated that the attractive force of bodies varies directly as their masses and inversely as the square of the distance between them. Put more simply, Newton's

'inverse square law of gravitation' says that if one body has a mass equal to $m1$ and a second body has a mass equal to $m2$ and they are separated by a distance r, then one body attracts the other with a force in proportion to: $m_1 m_2/r^2$.

Ancient people used to believe that there were only circles and spheres in the universe, because heavenly bodies were considered perfect as were those geometrical figures. This belief remained undisputed up to the time of Kepler. Then a series of observations on the position of Mars in the heavens were carried out by the Danish astronomer Tycho Brahe towards the end of the sixteenth century. Brahe presented the discrepancies between the experimental results and the statements which had been based on a very old and also inaccurate scientific philosophy.

The acute mind of Kepler, Brahe's assistant, uncovered the rules of movement which the stars obey. These laws of planetary motion are still valid today; the space probes follow them just as countless celestial bodies have followed them since the creation of the universe. Kepler's first law states that the planets revolve around the Sun in ellipses and that the Sun occupies one focus of the ellipse. The second law states that the radius vector (that is a line of variable length drawn to a curve from a fixed point) sweeps equal areas in equal times. Finally, the third law states that the square of the period of revolution is proportional to the cube of the major axis of the orbit.

Artificial satellites circle the Earth just as planets circle around the Sun. Astronauts aboard the capsule Gemini 9 *in June 1966 took this photograph of the* Agena *target vehicle with which they tried unsuccessfully to dock.*

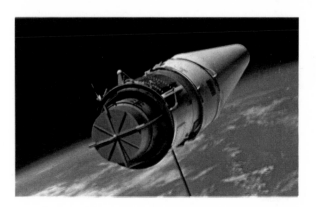

THE YEAR AND ITS SEASONS

The planet on which we live revolves around the Sun in space just as artificial satellites circle the Earth. The Earth, which has a small mass relative to that of the Sun, is bound by the Sun's attraction and is in a state of equilibrium. It can neither plunge towards the solar surface nor escape towards outer space. Therefore, the Earth travels submissively along its elliptical orbit around the Sun. The year is the period of time taken by our globe to complete its orbit.

Ancient people imagined the Earth to be the centre of the universe, and one of the most difficult changes of concept in science was that the Earth was not a stationary planet, but one which moved rapidly in space. Later on we shall discuss the Earth's removal from the eminent position it was thought to hold in the cosmos, and we shall see also that the Sun is not the central star in the universe, but let us now consider the main features of the Earth's orbital motion.

The Earth's Orbital Motion

Although the dimensions of our globe are enormous, measurements of the planet's orbit are much greater. The length of the terrestrial orbit is about 939,000,000 kilometres (nearly 584,000,000 miles) and its average radius is 149,500,000 kilometres (about 92,895,000 miles). These are huge figures compared with the 12,683 kilometres (about 7,927 miles) of the diameter of the Earth. In its gigantic orbit the planet travels at about 30 kilometres (approximately $18\frac{1}{2}$ miles) per second, but human senses cannot discern this speed for the same reason that they are unaware of the Earth's diurnal rotation.

The ellipse of the terrestrial orbit is very close to a circle. Between the perihelion and the aphelion, the distance from the Earth to the Sun varies by only 5,000,000 kilometres (3,107,000 miles) which is not great compared with the 149,000,000 kilometres (92,584,000 miles) which separate the Earth's surface from the fiery solar surface.

However, something occurs which appears strange to people living in the northern hemisphere: the perihelion falls on the first day of January and the aphelion on the first day of July. To understand the terms *perihelion* and *aphelion* we must consider a body travelling in an elliptical orbit around the Sun. It can be seen that such a body must at different times occupy positions at different distances from the Sun, which lies at one focal point of the ellipse. The body will be nearest to the Sun when it is at the end of the axis near to the main focus (this is called perihelion) and furthest from the Sun when it is at the opposite end of the main axis (this is aphelion). There is no relation between the variation in distance of the Earth from the Sun and the seasons. The reason for the change of seasons is due to the angle of the terrestrial axis.

The Seasons of the Year

If the axis which passes through the poles was perpendicular to the plane of the ecliptic (the name given to the imaginary plane on which the terrestrial and also the solar orbit lies), the seasons would not exist. We would still have our present climatic zones, because the Earth is spherical and the angle at which the Sun's rays strike it varies. The Sun's position among the stars shifts each day by about 1°—always towards the east—and if a chart were drawn of these shifts of degrees a single circular line could be drawn around the Earth which would form the ecliptic. The ecliptic is so-called because on that circular imaginary line around our globe the eclipses

of both the Sun and the Moon occur. However, even if the seasons did not exist, the deserts, the tropical forests, the temperate zone and the polar ice caps would still exist; but there would not be any variations; at the most, a slight variation in temperature would occur only twice a year—when the Earth was at the aphelion and the perihelion.

Under these imaginary conditions the days would have the same length forever and the seasonal phenomena, such as springtime blossoms and the golden autumn foliage, would be completely unknown. However, the terrestrial axis is inclined at an angle of

$23\frac{1}{2}°$ to an imaginary line perpendicular to the plane of the ecliptic. This angle remains constant just as the direction of the Earth's axis remains constant at whatever point along its orbit the Earth is found. Therefore, the inclination of the Sun's rays continually varies on each region of the Earth and that is the cause of the change of seasons.

On the 21st of December, the start of winter in the northern hemisphere, the South Pole is inclined towards the Sun and the North Pole away from it. The areas around the North Pole do not see the Sun because it remains below the horizon in spite

of the diurnal rotation, and because of the inclination of the axis. Slightly to the South in the latitude 59° 55′ N of Leningrad and Hudson Bay, the Sun rises just above the horizon for a very brief period each twenty-four hours, and there is a sort of twilight. In areas halfway between the North Pole and the equator, such as Italy or the Great Lakes region in North America, the day is much longer, although the Sun rises late, and sets early. At this time of the year, the Sun's rays strike the Earth at a low angle and they have very little warmth.

The Earth continues to move around the

This sequence of photographs was taken, from an island in northern Norway in June, of the Sun in the sky at midnight. Within the polar circles at the summer solstice the Sun does not set. This is an impressive consequence of the angle of inclination to the vertical of the Earth's axis.

Sun. Three months later, on March the 21st, spring begins; the boundary between the darkened hemisphere and the illuminated one passes exactly through the poles, thus each zone of the planet has twelve hours of day and twelve hours of night. The Sun's rays strike our hemisphere more directly and illuminate even the regions within the Arctic Circle, which were shrouded in night on the 21st of December. The air begins to warm up, the fields begin to turn green, flowers and trees begin to bud.

Three months later, on the 21st of June, the Earth in its orbit reaches the position exactly opposite the one it occupied on the 21st of December; therefore, the North Pole is inclined towards the Sun while the South Pole is inclined away from it. The regions within the Arctic Circle, although they rotate diurnally, do not enter the darkened hemisphere of the planet and therefore the Sun does not sink below their horizon. At midnight the sky is still lit by the Sun which shines low on the misty horizon, in the position opposite to the one it occupied at midday. In northern Russia, in Iceland and in the Canadian forests, the very short night is never completely dark. In southern Europe and America, the summer days are very long and the Sun's rays strike the Earth's surface almost vertically. The snows on the mountains begin to disappear from even the highest peaks.

At the start of autumn, on the 21st of September, the conditions of the 21st of March are repeated; day and night are the same length on all parts of the Earth. The inclination of the Sun's rays increases, the days become shorter and the temperature starts to fall. The trees' autumnal leaves appear. From the north come mists and fog, and the Earth has almost completed its annual orbit.

Solstices and Equinoxes

The four fundamental positions which our planet assumes in a year are called *solstices* and *equinoxes*. The word *solstice* comes from two Latin words, *sol* meaning Sun and *stare* meaning to stand still. *Equinox* comes from the Latin *aequus* meaning equal and *nox* which means night. The solstices occur when one of the poles is inclined towards the Sun. The equinoxes occur when the boundary of the illuminated hemisphere passes through both poles and night and day are of equal duration. In the northern hemisphere, the 21st of

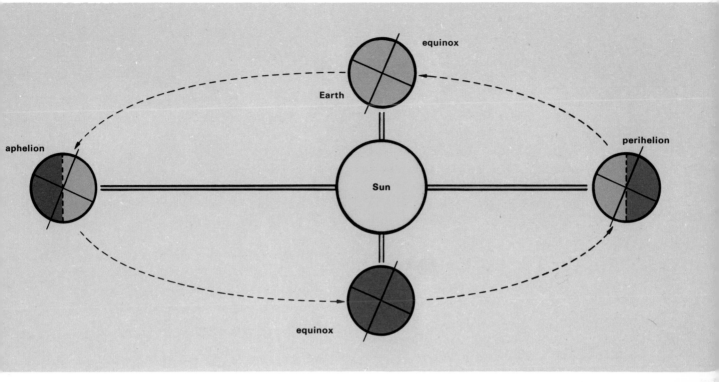

Above: *The orbit of the Earth and the resulting seasons. While the Earth moves around the Sun, the angle of inclination of its axis remains constant and the poles pass through extreme conditions of illumination and obscurity. On the* left *the Earth is at aphelion and the northern hemisphere is in summer. On the* right *it is at perihelion and it is summer in the southern hemisphere. At the two intermediate points (the equinoxes) the days and nights are equal in length.*

Opposite: *The fact that opposite seasons exist at the same time on the Earth creates strange combinations of conditions: while in the northern hemisphere winter attracts skiers to the snow slopes,* above; *in the southern hemisphere summer calls the water sports enthusiasts to the sea,* below.

December is the winter solstice and the 21st of June is the summer solstice; the 21st of March is the spring equinox and the 21st of September is the autumn equinox. In the southern hemisphere the positions are reversed, which is natural considering that the two poles are inclined alternately towards the Sun, and that when on one pole the Sun shines throughout the day and night, the other pole is plunged in the polar night. In the countries of the southern hemisphere the summer starts on the 21st of December and the winter on the 21st of June. When in North America and Europe the snow attracts thousands of skiing enthusiasts to the white slopes which offer an inviting prospect, in Africa and South America and in Australia, the beaches are crowded and the weather is warm. Christmas is celebrated in the

splendours of the summer Sun. When the waves of the Mediterranean Sea are warm under a hot Sun, the Australian Alps are white with snow and the cold winds of winter sweep across the pampas of the Argentine. Together there are extreme seasons at the same time on the Earth as a result of the inclination of its axis.

Apart from the periods of the equinoxes and the solstices, the days and nights are not of equal length. The length of the longest day and the shortest day in the year depends on the latitude where one lives. In London, which is at $51\frac{1}{2}°$ latitude, the shortest day lasts eight hours and the longest about sixteen hours. In New York City, which is at $40°$ latitude, the shortest day lasts about nine hours and the longest about fifteen hours.

THE CALENDAR AND MAGNETISM

Primitive man was ignorant of the laws of nature which regulate the passage of our planet around the Sun, but he must have noticed with wonder the changes each season brought to the world around him. Above all, living on the food provided by the Earth and the waters, he must have been struck by the periodic events which influenced his choice of food and the way in which he must live.

When man became an agriculturalist and created stable settlements, the need to understand and anticipate the rhythm of nature became a part of his social life. He had already found that in summer objects projected shadows very much shorter than in winter; therefore, it was fairly easy to ascertain that on a certain day at the beginning of summer, the shadows were the shortest possible. Once it was determined what the minimum length of shadows of columns or of suitable monoliths were, it then became possible to determine the annual arrival of the summer. It is believed that the Stonehenge ruins on Salisbury Plain may originally have been constructed in order to determine the seasons. The Inca Indians of Peru used this system. But other ancient people turned to the stars. Since the circular movement of the Earth makes the starry sky appear different at various periods during the year, it is possible to look at certain constellations to determine the start of the seasons and particular events, such as the ripening of grain, which are related to them. The ancient Egyptian astronomers, who have left us many records of their work, followed this system.

Left: *An astronomical observatory (1718 to 1734) at Jaipur in India.*

Below: *The ruins of Stonehenge on Salisbury Plain in Wiltshire, England.*

Opposite: *Harvesting the crops in July (Fifteenth century French painting).*

The Calendar

Many thousands of years before Jesus was born, a calendar was used in Egypt which divided the year into 365 days. The priests who were the custodians of this knowledge did not know the exact interval between the two equinoxes—the so-called tropical year—which is not exactly 365 days, but 365 days, five hours, 48 minutes and 46 seconds. A little less than six hours per year would seem to make little difference in a yearly calendar; but in a few centuries the seasons are turned around, because the extra hours make the calendar indicate summer when in fact it is winter. A remedy was found by inserting extra days. The extra day found in the month of February in a leap year is simply a system for making the calendar we use agree with the true movement of the Sun.

The introduction into the calendar of an extra day every four years was made by Julius Caesar (in 46 B.C.). If the difference between the true year and the calendar year were exactly six hours, all would have been well. But we have already seen that it is a little less, and therefore there had to be a second reform.

In 1582, Pope Gregory made certain rules so that the calendar would remain valid and conform to astronomical data for an indefinite period. In order to correct the errors in former calendars, a certain number of days were suppressed (eleven in Britain in 1752) and then to prevent further displacement the rule was established that for every hundred years (1600, 1700, 1800, etc.) only those years exactly divisible by 400 should be counted as leap years (*e.g.* 1600). The calendar was called the *Gregorian Calendar* and it is the one we use today. In the chapter on the Moon, the reasons for the particular divisions of our calendar into the months and the weeks will be discussed.

We have now completed a brief examination of the Earth's movements and have discussed some of the information needed to understand the measurement of time. Now let us turn to the magnetism of the Earth.

Terrestrial Magnetism

The Earth's magnetism constantly rules the needles of the compasses and creates a zone in space around our planet in which particular phenomena can occur.

For almost four centuries we have known that our planet acts like an enormous magnet. The physician to Queen Elizabeth I, named William Gilbert (1543–1603), discovered this fact. In 1600 he published a book on the magnet noting that the effect of the Earth on a compass was similar to that obtained with a piece of magnetite, an iron mineral with magnetic properties. If a compass is placed over a magnetic bar Gilbert's discovery can be verified: each magnetic pole of the needle is attracted by the opposing pole of the bar, so that the needle points in a direction parallel to the bar itself.

The Earth also has magnetic poles, which do not, however, coincide with the ends of its axis of rotation but which fall within the polar circles. In the Arctic the magnetic pole is situated at the extreme limit of Canadian territory, in the heart of the islands and frozen straits extending from Greenland to Alaska. In the Antarctic the magnetic pole is found in Victoria Land near the edge of the most impenetrable and desolate plateau in the world.

If some iron filings are placed on a sheet of paper and the paper is placed over the poles of a horseshoe-shaped magnet, the filings arrange themselves along the lines of force

Left: *An ornamental pocket compass. The needle of the compass is permanently orientated in the direction of the Earth's magnetic poles.*

Below: *The Earth with its magnetic poles; and a section through the lines of force perfectly analogous to the lines of force around an ordinary magnet. All these lines of force constitute the magnetic field of the Earth.*

Opposite page: *If we examine this modern, simple but elegant compass we note its pure practicality which is in marked contrast to the superfluous ornamentation of the compass above left. At one time the pocket compass was a popular present, and the phenomenon of the needle pointing to the North was regarded with curiosity.*

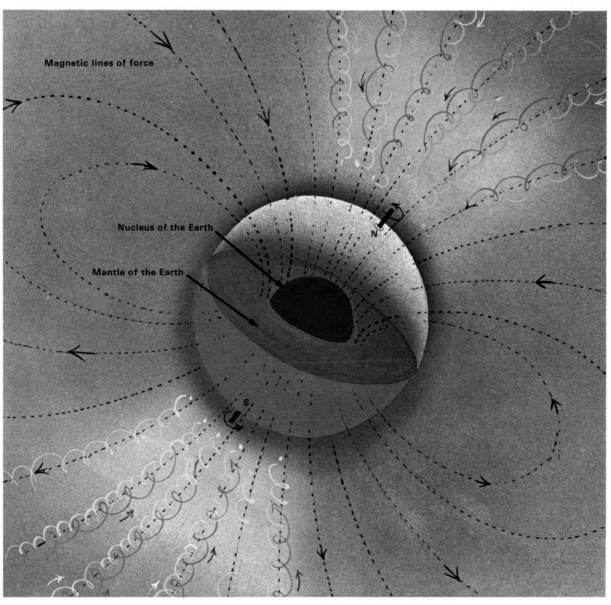

Magnetic lines of force

Nucleus of the Earth

Mantle of the Earth

emanating from the poles of the magnet and which join one pole to the other. Thus the presence of a magnetic field around the magnet is revealed.

In the same way, a magnetic field exists in space around the Earth; but although the Earth is a sphere, the lines of force all round it create a field with a pear-shaped surface. The lines of force are not spherically shaped because of solar winds. This 'surface of force' field is called the terrestrial magnetosphere.

When *Explorer I*, the pioneer artificial American satellite, was put into orbit in space on 31st January 1958, our knowledge of the magnetosphere was rather limited. But the measurements which *Explorer* transmitted on the intensity of solar radiation, and on the presence of electrically-charged particles around the Earth, outlined immediately the characteristics of the Earth's magnetic field and enabled scientists to discover its structure and other aspects which had not previously been known. The American physicist James A. Van Allen, who together with a group of specialists collected the data from *Explorer I* and successive satellites, was able to demonstrate that the Earth is surrounded by two invisible belts, arranged along the surfaces of force of the magnetosphere where the particles become trapped and must circulate from one magnetic pole to the other. These are the Van Allen belts.

The first of these belts starts at 1,000–1,300 kilometres (620–800 miles) above the Earth's surface and extends up to 4,000–5,000 kilometres (2,490–3,100 miles). The second extends from a height of 14,000 kilometres (8,700 miles) to about 24,000–25,000 kilometres (14,900–15,530 miles). In these belts the particles coming mainly from the Sun reach a concentration which would be dangerous for astronauts who had to stay there for any length of time. However, the belts safeguard life on Earth from the particles. Fortunately, the two great rings produced by the terrestrial magnetic field are wide open over the poles; and future manned space craft may use this peculiar feature, if necessary.

It is at points corresponding to the magnetic poles that a part of the circulating particles enter the upper atmosphere and illuminate the rarefied gases which form the highest atmospheric layers. The phenomenon which is derived from this, the formation of the polar auroras, has already been described.

At this point, the description of the Earth, as a world and as a planet, is complete. Therefore, the next step in understanding the universe is to look towards the distant sky and to examine the Moon and the Sun, the two main lights in our sky.

A section through the Van Allen belts, discovered in 1958, which collect electrically charged particles between the surfaces of force of the terrestrial magnetosphere.

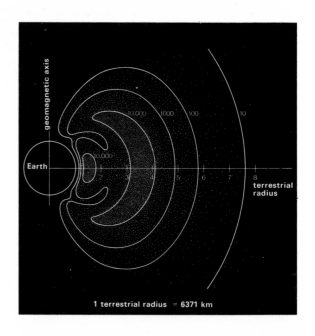

Part Two

THE MOON AND THE SUN

THE MOON AND ITS PHASES

At night when the crescent Moon shines and the side facing us is less than half illuminated, a pair of binoculars enables one to make fascinating observations. Between the dark and the illuminated parts of the lunar disc there appears a frayed line of light and shadow and this reveals the mountains of Earth's satellite. The Moon is so close to us that only slight magnification is enough to show the general features of its surface.

Our Satellite's Position

When other astronomical distances are considered, the distance from the Earth to the Moon appears negligible. However, the distance is not small when compared with terrestrial measurements—it is, on the average, 384,000 kilometres (238,607 miles). A spaceship can make the journey in less than three days. Assuming that we could use everyday means to travel in space, the distance would be a true abyss. Imagine a bridge stretching from the Earth to the Moon: a car running without stopping at 100 kilometres (62 miles) per hour would take 145 days and 20 hours to complete the journey. An imaginary pedestrian crossing the same bridge who was walking at 5 kilometres (3 miles) per hour would take eight years and ninety-seven days to arrive at his lunar destination even if he never stopped for a rest!

Primitive man, who saw the stars as mysterious phenomena suspended in the vault above his head, had no idea of the distance from the Earth to the Moon nor did he think of the Moon as a world in itself. He regarded the Earth's satellite as a friendly light which broke the darkness of the night, but he also associated it with fear. For those reasons, he deified the pale star and combined its opposing attributes in the gods. In ancient Egypt, the Moon was personified as the Goddess Isis, friend of the Sun, and also as the God Tot, who was secretary of the tribunal of the afterlife. According to the Greeks, the Moon was Artemis, the beautiful huntress goddess who wandered through the woods armed with a bow, and also Hecate, the goddess of magic, darkness and spirits.

In search of the true order of the universe, ancient philosophers tried to assess our satellite's position in the heavens. In the sixth century B.C. Anaximander of Miletus in Asia Minor believed that the Moon and the Sun were the heavenly bodies furthest from us and he thought that the Moon was the most remote. Three centuries later,

Above: *The Goddess Isis was the most important personification of the Moon in ancient Egypt.*

Opposite: *Full Moon over the towers and walls of the ancient Moorish city of Avila in Spain.*

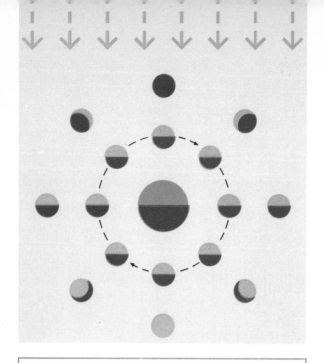

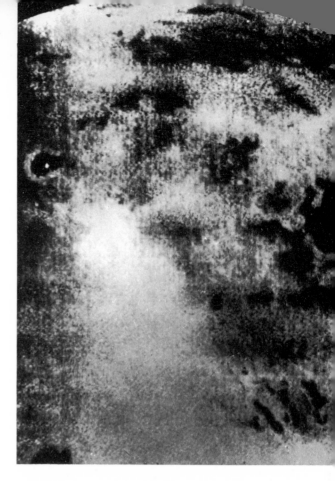

Above: *The phases of the Moon. The different positions of the Moon in its orbit are shown in the inner circle; the views as seen from the Earth are shown in the outer circle.*

Right: *A photograph of the Moon taken from the Russian space probe* Lunik III.

Aristarchus of Samos made the first attempt to determine geometrically the distance from the Earth to the Moon. His results were not far from the truth.

Then, slowly, with continued measuring and with more precise knowledge of the Earth which serves as a base for the determination of the distance to the Moon, man began to calculate more precisely. Now our knowledge is extremely accurate and today's scientists are able to choose the places where Moon probes will land.

Like the Earth, the Moon has a form which is almost that of a perfect sphere. Its diameter is 3,480 kilometres (2,162 miles), or less than one-third of the average terrestrial diameter. Forty-nine spheres equal to the volume of the Moon would be needed to equal the volume of our globe, yet the lunar mass is equal to only one-eighty-first part of the mass of the Earth. So the Moon is much lighter in mass than the Earth. Surface gravity on the Moon is only one-sixth of that on Earth. As a result, the Moon has been unable to retain sufficient molecules to form even a primordial atmosphere. The Moon is a dreary world, lacking a covering of air which would colour the

sky or support life, and it has no defence against the cold of space and the violent radiation of the Sun. Because of its lack of atmosphere, its intense cold and the high concentration of radiation, the Moon cannot possibly sustain any form of life.

The Moon's Orbital Motion

Following Kepler's laws, the Moon moves around the Earth in an orbit which is nearly circular in shape. The Moon rises in the east and sets in the west, in approximately the way the sky above Earth moves; this appearance is produced by the terrestrial rotation. From one night to the next the Moon also moves in relation to the constellations; this is the effect of its real orbital motion which makes it move from the west towards the east and which retards its appearance in the sky by 38 to 66 minutes each day.

Directly dependent on its orbital motion are those periodically variable, but recurrent, aspects called the Moon's phases. The Moon does not have a light of its own but is lit by the Sun. When the Moon is positioned between the Earth and the Sun we cannot see it because the darkened side of its hemisphere is turned towards us, and this is called the phase of the 'New Moon'. Then transported by its motion, it emerges from the darkness and starts to show a portion of its illuminated hemisphere in the form of a thin crescent. From one night to the next, while it regularly sets later each day, the crescent increases in size until, after about a week, half of the illuminated hemisphere is perfectly visible and this is the 'first quarter'.

After the Moon's first quarter, which appears as a half-Moon, our satellite continues waxing until it becomes 'gibbous'. The Moon in this stage (the name for it seems unusual but comes from the Latin word *gibbus* meaning hump) rises later and later in the afternoon and shines far into the small hours of the night. It blots out many stars during this period.

Continuing to set later, the Moon is seen in the evening in the east, and is gradually more fully illuminated. After about fifteen days, the Moon rises almost exactly at the same time as the Sun sets and attains its maximum height above the horizon at midnight; it is in line with the Sun, but at a point opposite the celestial sphere and we, therefore, see it completely illuminated. This is the phase of the 'Full Moon'.

After this, the Moon is seen very late at night while its illuminated hemisphere gradually becomes smaller. Again we see the half-illuminated disc and this phase is called the 'last quarter'.

Then the thin crescent shape appears again, always turned towards the Sun and therefore inverted with respect to the attitude or position which we saw first in the evening. The Moon slowly plunges into the light of dawn and finally disappears in the Sun's aureole. Thus we have returned to the phase of the 'New Moon'.

The complete cycle, called a synodic revolution, takes twenty-nine days, twelve hours and forty-four minutes. This is the lunar month, a very old division of time. Although ancient man did not know the exact duration of the lunar month, as we now do, he found it useful to measure time based on this cycle which is longer than the rhythm of day and night but shorter and easier to determine than the long solar year. He could determine the commencement of

the cycle by watching the first appearance of the thin crescent Moon, after the New Moon had appeared in the western sky lit by the red glow of sunset. Long ago, this cyclic reappearance of the Moon was solemnly celebrated.

There are four phases of the Moon which occur during the month and these fall about every seven days. This suggested another division of time: the week. The Hebrews used it even before Moses, and this period of time has been retained up to the present day. Work in the modern world is governed by it.

The month, too, has remained in the calendar but it no longer follows the Moon's phases. Since the duration of the lunar month is not a round fraction of the year, it was not possible to maintain it without increasing its length by a suitable amount; and this has been done since very ancient times.

Any discussion of the lunar phases would not be complete without a mention of the so-called 'Earth light' which illuminates the dark part of the Moon, in the evening or the morning, when it is first a crescent. At this time, the light of the terrestrial hemisphere, which is lit by the Sun, is reflected on the lunar surface and banishes the darkness from the face of the Moon. When the glow of sunset dies and night advances the Moon can be seen from Earth like a globe shaded and bounded by a brilliant crescent.

Apart from its movement in orbit around the Earth, the Moon has a rotational movement about its axis, which is very slow and which is of the same duration as its orbital period. As a result of this the Moon's surface as seen from the Earth is always the same side or hemisphere.

Half of the Moon's surface is hidden but telescopes reveal limited peripheral areas of the hidden side which are visible as a result of small oscillations of the satellite, called librations. The other side of the Moon remained, until a few years ago, a part of the universe absolutely cut off from any possibility of investigation. However, in 1959, the Russian space probe *Lunik III* started exploration and this part of the universe is no longer unknown. Magnificent *close-up* photographs of the Moon and its surface have been taken by Russian and American spacecraft.

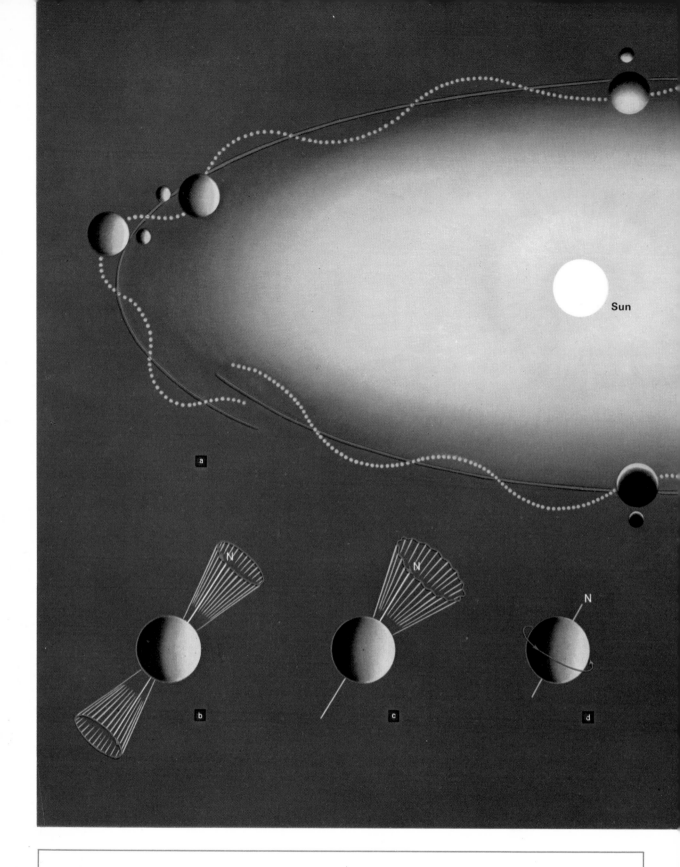

Diagram showing the movements of the Earth, the Moon and the Sun. Fig. a shows the movement of the Earth-Moon system around the Sun; note that the movement changes every year. The same variation is emphasised in fig. e. In figs. b, c and d we can see the various movements completed by the Earth while rotating on its axis. In fig. d we have indicated the most important of these movements, that of rotation, which occurs once in about 24 hours. Fig. b is a schematic representation of the movement which the imaginary

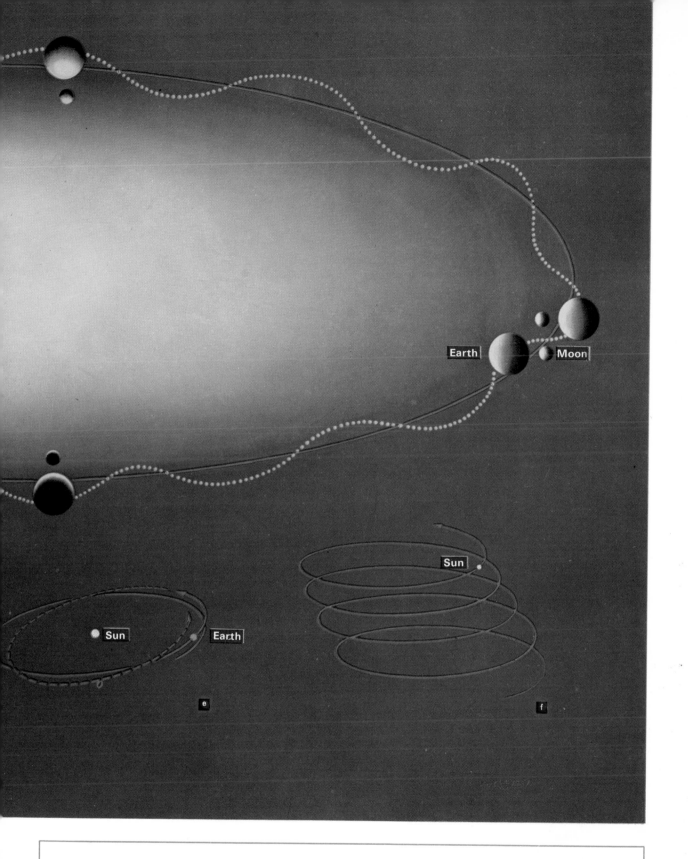

extension of the terrestrial axis describes in space as a result of the procession of the equinoxes. It describes an imaginary double cone which is irregular because of nutation (the oscillation of the Earth's axis), as in fig. c, and which is completed in about 27,000 years. The effect of this movement is that in 5,600 years' time the pole star will be Alpha in Cepheus; in 12,000 years it will be Vega; and in 29,000 years it will return to its present position. In fig. f the movement of the Solar System around the centre of the galaxy is shown.

THE FACE OF THE SATELLITE

When the Moon is full and lightens the sky with its brightness, its 'face' is lined with marks which seem to look at us with a smile. This appearance gave rise to myths and superstitions about the 'man in the Moon'. Man sought in ancient times to clarify the enigma of that face with the help of his imagination; he thought the face could be the image of the ocean reflected in a mirror, or the various manifestations of ethereal substances, or vapours which rose from the Earth. But the most daring minds imagined mountains and valleys on the Moon, and they even supposed it was inhabited. The Pythagorean philosophers (between the fifth and sixth centuries B.C.) thought that men who were fifteen times taller and more robust than Earth's inhabitants lived on the Moon and that there were animals and plants more beautiful than those on Earth.

In the winter of 1609–1610, Galileo turned his first telescope towards the Moon. A new, completely unexpected world was revealed to his gaze. The marks which outlined the 'face' appeared as flat grey expanses; and on the bright parts of the disc there were craters and mountains which had never been seen before. In that moment a new geography was born called *selenography* (from Selene, one of the Greek personifications of the Moon), the study of the Moon's surface.

With the beginning of telescopic study, the mountains of the satellite received names for the first time. The Italian Jesuit priest Giovanni Riccioli, named many areas of the lunar surface in the mid-1600's. He called the craters by the names of scientists and philosophers, he baptised mountains and named the 'seas'—those grey expanses which outline the Moon's 'face'. Riccioli's names were retained and added to modern lunar maps which have been extended to the invisible side of the Moon revealed by space probes. The same names appear on the detailed maps which the big space centres are preparing for the men destined to take part in the exploration of the satellite.

The Desolate Surface

The Moon, which awaits these space explorers, is a world of rock and dust, more arid than the hottest terrestrial desert. Because there is no atmosphere there is no water on its surface; nor are there clouds, rain, oceans, fields or forests.

It is most probable that there is no life on the Moon. The absence of air and water implies not only that there are no living things as we know them, but also that planetary life is impossible. Even if the Earth were without animals and vegetation it would be a living planet because the rains would erode the mountains, the rivers would drag the rock fragments into the valleys and the coastal deposits would transform the seaboards while elsewhere the movement of the waves would continually alter the rocks which emerge from the seas.

On the Moon this cannot happen; in the so-called 'seas' there is not a single drop of water and above them not even the smallest cloud can condense. In general, the so-called 'seas' or *maria* (from the Latin word for sea: *mare*) are large, more or less circular plains, which are sunk below the general level of the lunar surface. The *maria* are the lowest areas on the Moon—we do not know how 'deep' they can go because their slopes are very gentle.

Seen from the Moon, the celestial vault is

Opposite top: *The lunar Antarctic. This spectacular relief photograph shows craters of all sizes on the Moon. The photograph was taken with a large telescope during the Moon's last quarter; however, the smallest astronomical telescope enables one to appreciate all the beauty of the lunarscape. It can also be seen in miniature if one uses a pair of prismatic binoculars.*

Opposite below: *The first drawings of the Moon with its craters and its mountains prepared by Galileo in 1610.*

perpetually dark and the stars are always visible. Among the constellations the radiant Sun moves very slowly and the days on the Moon last two weeks. While the Sun is almost immobile in the sky, the rocky lunar surface reaches temperatures of 100° C. (212° F.) or more. During the night, which is as long as the day, the same surface will fall in temperature to 150° below zero C. (230° below zero F.). Because of the brilliant sunlight and lack of atmosphere, lunarscapes have no soft shadows.

On the Moon there is no aerial perspective like that on Earth which diminishes the distances; the mountains which arise on the horizon can be seen as clearly as the nearest objects. When the Sun rises, its first rays cut the darkness like the light from a projector; when it sets, night falls on the lunarscape like a black pall. There is never even the slightest breeze or the faintest echo of a falling stone; enormous landslides could fall for miles without creating the slightest sound. However, despite the fact that there is no colour visible on the Moon comparable to Earth sunsets and sunrises, the stars as seen from

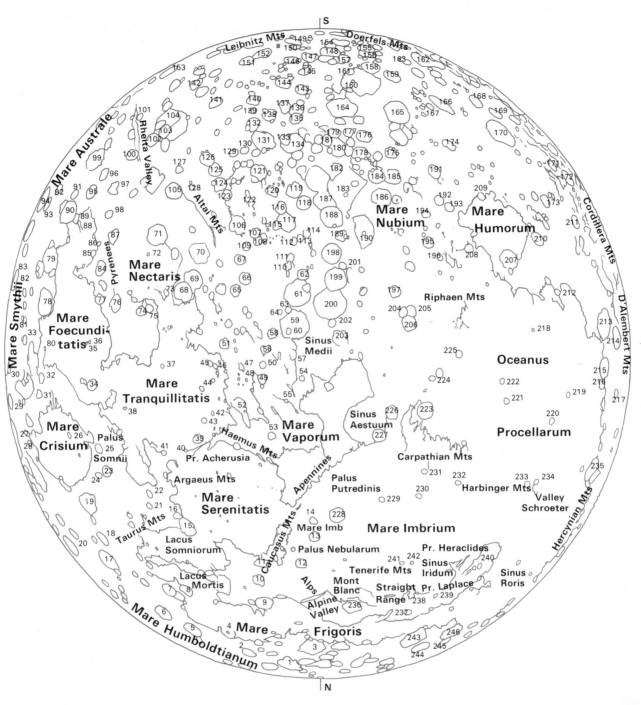

our satellite shine more brightly in the skies and many more are to be seen although they do not twinkle because of the lack of atmosphere.

These incredible lunarscapes can be seen in the photographs taken by the space probes and manned spacecraft. These photographs have enabled objects several yards across to be measured; and cameras on the probes which have landed on the Moon's surface have taken detailed pictures in which it is possible to count even the smallest stones. Together with panoramic views, these have

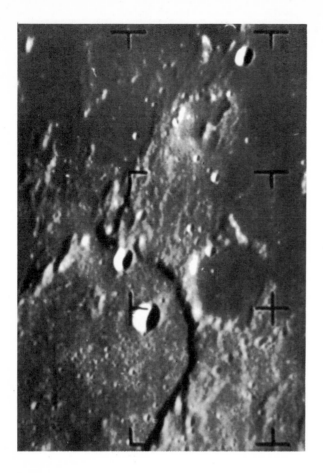

given scientists precious information on the surface of the satellite. Up to a few years ago it was thought that the surface was covered with a blanket of dust formed of microscopic meteorites and the break up of the rocks caused by the enormous temperature changes. Now we know that this layer is very thin and that the lunar soil, in spite of its being more porous and softer than the rocks of our mountains, is sufficiently hard to allow the landing of space ships. This soil, like certain lavas and volcanic ashes, reflects only seven per cent of the sunlight, an indication that on the Moon we see the primitive crust unaltered by great geological events as on our planet. This poses the problem of the origin of the Moon's surface.

Above: *The two photographs show the extraordinary difference between the lunar surface as seen from afar and that of the Earth. On the* right: *the Himalayan mountains photographed from the American space capsule* Gemini 5 *in August 1965. On the* left: *the lunar crater Gauricus photographed from the American space probe* Ranger 7 *(1964).*

Below: *A photograph of great historic importance—the first photographs of the lunar rocks taken on the surface of the Moon from the Russian probe* Lunik IX *in February 1966.*

The Moon's Craters

In a telescope, even a modest one, the overall view of the lunarscape is one of the most beautiful astronomical observations. The great circular craters which are spread over the Moon's surface are most conspicuous, edged with bright light and filled with black shadows. This relief has a particular

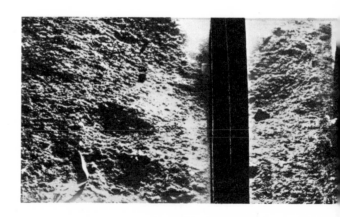

structure; the internal floors of the craters are lower than the surrounding plains. Their sizes are often enormous. The crater Tycho, one of the most beautiful in the southern hemisphere, has a diameter of 87 kilometres (54 miles) and its rim has an altitude of 6,157 metres (20,200 feet). Still larger is Clavius, with a diameter of 230 kilometres (143 miles); it contains scattered hills and minor craters, and is delineated by a mountainous ring which rises to 5,586 metres (18,620 feet) above its base. These heights remind us of the great mountains of the Andes, but we must not imagine the Moon to be like the Peruvian mountains. Moon craters always have gentle, often terraced, slopes and even if, here and there, there are steep inclines, they are very different from the severe profiles of many mountains on the Earth.

There are a great number of craters which cover the entire surface of the Moon. The largest contain smaller secondary craters. Often, in the medium-sized craters, there is a central peak; but the smallest ones are simple cup-shaped holes in the lunar surface. In the past, their formation was attributed entirely to energy within the Moon through phenomena similar to those which occur in our volcanoes. Two French astronomers, M. Loewy and P. Puiseux, formulated a hypothesis at the beginning of the present century, which was generally accepted. According to their theory, the Moon, while cooling at the beginning of its history, released from within large quantities of gas which formed bubbles in the soft lunar crust; the bubbles burst and left scars in the form of craters. However, in the nineteenth century the English astronomer Richard Proctor (1837–1888) formed the idea that the lunar craters were the result of the impact of meteorites. The meteorite hypothesis has taken precedence in recent decades and the ideas of Loewy and Puiseux have been abandoned. The similarity of proportion and general aspect of the craters on the Moon is quite like the effect of an artillery or aerial bombardment on the Earth's surface.

There are some meteoric craters on the Earth, but they are quite small when compared with the enormous framework of terrestrial relief. Proof of the impact of meteorites on the surface of the Moon cannot be sought on Earth. The lunar crust is primitive and very ancient, while the Earth's crust has been completely modified and altered by the changes which have taken place throughout the different geological eras. Therefore, hypotheses must be checked on the Moon itself by looking for traces of the meteorites whose impact gave rise to the craters. It is probable that scientists and astronauts will also find some indication of volcanic activity, but this will probably not affect present ideas of the formation of craters very much.

These, then, are the essential features of the Moon, a desolate world, and yet marvellous to contemplate through the telescope and fascinating for men who seek new adventures in space. Astronomers of the future will be able to set their telescopes upon the Moon's surface and study the stars with great ease because there will be no interference in the unclouded lunar sky. These scientists to come may well marvel that men in the 1950's and 1960's were able to learn so much about the sky with the relatively poor atmospheric conditions on the Earth obscuring their research attempts.

TIDES AND ECLIPSES

Tides

Every day the level of our oceans oscillates rhythmically as a result of tidal phenomenon. Twice every twenty-four hours the waters recede and uncover the muds and sands below high-water mark or the polished rocks where marine creatures cling; and twice a day the waters advance over the shores that they had abandoned earlier. Tides are not governed by the Earth, but mainly by the Moon's gravitational force.

In the third century B.C. Eratosthenes of Cyrene (276–196 B.C.) first related the Moon to the pulsation of the waters on Earth. But the exact explanation of tides was available only after Sir Isaac Newton had defined the laws of gravitation.

As a result of the Moon's gravitational attraction the water molecules on the side of the Earth facing the satellite tend to rise towards it. On the opposite side of the globe the water rises because the gravitational attraction of the satellite is not as great on the surface as it is at the Earth's centre. The result is that over the entire circumference of the globe the water rises in two bulges which are separated by two depressions. The bulges follow the Moon and move around the Earth in about twenty-four hours and fifty minutes (the period of the terrestrial rotation plus the daily retardation of the Moon's rising). Thus during each day there are two high tides and two low tides.

The Sun also influences this phenomenon but to a much smaller extent than the Moon. The Sun's distance from the Earth is too great to have a great effect on tides, in spite of its enormous mass. The relatively small Moon exerts an influence on the waters more than twice that of the gigantic Sun. However, the action of the two bodies can be added together when the Sun, Moon and Earth are aligned (at the New Moon and at the Full Moon); tides a little higher than normal occur at those times. The high tide level is at a minimum, however, when the Moon is in its first or last quarter, that is in an intermediate position between the New Moon and the Full Moon.

The conformation of the ocean floor, marine currents, and the variable structure of the coastlines influence the tides and change their effects from one place to another on the Earth. The oscillations vary from a few feet to fifty or sixty feet. Perhaps the most famous tidal effect is found at Mt St Michel, an island just off the coast of Brittany on which there is a renowned ancient abbey. At high tide, it is surrounded by the waters of the Channel; but when the tide is low, the surrounding rocks are completely uncovered and the land seems to extend as far as the eye can see.

The Moon's attraction (coupled with that of the Sun) makes itself felt on the equatorial bulge of the Earth and causes a slow displacement of the direction of the terrestrial axis in space; this is called the precessional movement. The consequences of this movement will be shown in the discussion of the constellations.

However, now we shall investigate the Moon's influence on the life of our planet. Mediaeval science held that everything on the Earth followed the rhythm of the phases of the Moon and that with the development of the Moon from New Moon to Full Moon, all animals and plants grew, and all declined with its waning. Still we must not forget that the Moon collects and reflects on to the Earth a small part of the solar radiation and thus it is perhaps possible to explain certain correlations between the Moon's presence in the heavens and some biological or meteorological events on Earth.

Eclipses

The Moon is not limited to demonstrating its variable phases in the heavens and to bathing our landscapes in light; it also displays the extremely impressive spectacles of the eclipses.

On some occasions it momentarily hides (or eclipses) the Sun; on other occasions the

Sun

Moon   Earth

Above: *The tides of the Earth's oceans are the result of the combined gravitational attraction of the Sun and the Moon.*
Below: *The famous island of Mont St Michel off the Brittany coast at low and at high tide.*
Below, right: *Marine molluscs, which live attached to rocks which rise out of the seas, are left high and dry twice a day by the tides.*

Moon is eclipsed or submerged in the Earth's shadow which is projected in space as a dark cone. If the lunar orbit fell exactly in the plane of the terrestrial orbit, at every New Moon our satellite would obscure the Sun and on each Full Moon it would be obscured by the Earth. The eclipses would then have a monthly periodicity. Since the two orbits are inclined at a certain angle to each other, the eclipses are produced only when the alignment of the Sun, Moon and Earth (or Sun, Earth and Moon) occurs at the moment when the plane of the lunar orbit intersects the plane of the ecliptic. For that reason, eclipses are rare phenomena.

Hidden in the Earth's shadow during the eclipses, the Full Moon loses its splendour but is not completely obscured. A small part of the Sun's light is refracted by the Earth's atmosphere and reaches the Moon's disc, illuminating it with a dark red glow. A gloomy sunset colouring descends on the satellite. This copper-coloured Moon appears strange in the sky where the stars blaze as on the nights of a New Moon. When it enters the

Earth's shadow at the start of the phenomenon (and when it leaves), a perfectly black arc bathed at its edge by a bluish light is projected on its face and this shows part of our planet's profile. Since ancient times this appearance has justly been considered as one of the proofs of the Earth's spherical shape.

During the eclipses, the red hot lunar rocks and the slopes of the craters which burn in the Sun are plunged into a night more profound than our polar nights, because on the Moon there is an eclipse of the Sun. Since the Moon lacks the reserve of heat which is maintained by the Earth's atmosphere, the temperature plummets to minimum values. It does not always suffer these consequences because the Moon can cross, at the edge of the terrestrial shadow, a zone of space where the Sun is not completely covered by our globe; then a penumbral eclipse occurs which affects the satellite with a faint dark shadow, sometimes only visible with astronomical instruments. When the Moon passes through the edge of the dark cone of shadow cast by the Earth it is only partly affected by the shadow and a partial eclipse occurs.

From all places on the Earth where the Moon is above the horizon it is possible to see a lunar eclipse as it occurs, if the weather conditions are right. However, when there is an eclipse of the Sun things are very different. The small shadow which the Moon projects on to the Earth cannot possibly cover it, but it passes over the surface as a result of the terrestrial rotation. If we are in the path of the advancing shadow, we see the Sun completely covered in a total eclipse. For those who are outside the shadow but close to its path, only a part of the disc is hidden by the Moon in a partial eclipse. Beyond the lunar umbra and penumbra, the sun shines freely on the terrestrial landscape and there is no trace of an eclipse. The term umbra applies to the complete shadow of the Earth or the Moon in an eclipse, and the penumbra is the partial shadow which surrounds the complete shadow of either of these opaque bodies.

This explains why an eclipse of the Sun is much rarer and much shorter in length than an eclipse of the Moon. While a lunar eclipse can last more than two hours under the most

Above: *A total eclipse of the Moon. The Earth's shadow covers the satellite which remains visible, suffused with a copper-coloured light.*

Opposite: *The marvellous spectacle of the total eclipse of the Sun. The Moon is hiding the Sun's entire disc, but the solar protuberances are apparent and the corona is visible.*

favourable conditions, a total eclipse of the Sun cannot last more than a few minutes. However, during this very short period, astronomers can follow the Sun and undertake research of great importance. The Sun, masked by the Moon outside the Earth's atmosphere, provides special conditions for observation. It is necessary for students of the Sun to go to the so-called 'total eclipse belt' when an eclipse occurs. To wait for this event in observatories is useless.

In Britain the last total solar eclipse, in 1927, was observed in England and Scotland for less than a minute. In America, total eclipses have occurred only five times since the turn of the century. The occurrence of any sort of eclipse in a particular place is extremely rare. Modern astronomy is, however, aware of the workings of these phenomena, and with the improved understanding which has been attained with respect to celestial movements, it is now possible to

predict well in advance all the details of eclipses of the Sun and Moon.

By a very particular chance, the Sun and the Moon can appear in the same area in the sky from the Earth. The slight oscillations of the distance produced by the elliptical shape of the terrestrial and lunar orbits can result in the Moon only partly covering the Sun; then there is an annular eclipse. More frequently, the satellite's black disc covers the brilliant Sun. This happened in the eclipse of 1961. Then the spectacle is truly exciting.

At the beginning of an eclipse, daylight fades slowly while the Moon conceals the Sun. When the Sun is reduced to a very thin crescent, a dim bluish twilight falls over the landscape, while the air becomes colder and animals clearly show signs of fear. The great shadow of the Moon quickly advances from west to east. The crescent Sun becomes thinner until it appears as no more than a thread, then for a moment it looks like a diamond mounted on a very fine ring of light. Suddenly, the black Moon takes the Sun's place. Almost as quickly an unreal night descends on everything, and the entire sky is tinged with an incredible, dark blue colour. The brightest stars appear like minute, stationary sparks. Around the black Sun a pearly aureole is clearly visible; it is known as the solar corona. As one watches, the solar prominences appear, slowly, at the edge of the Sun itself. For a few minutes these sights hold spectators utterly spellbound; then the light gradually returns.

Occultations

As the Moon goes on its journey through the sky, it moves in front of any star or any planet which lies in its path in the same way as it passes the Sun. Although when this phenomena occurs the star or planet in the Moon's path is 'eclipsed', astronomers call this event an occultation.

Because the Moon does not travel on exactly the same path each month, the stars or planets it occults are not always the same. Occultations can be seen from the Earth at various times and locations. The relative sizes and positions in the sky of the Earth, the Moon and the stars or planet which the Moon passes, all determine the exact spot from which an occultation will be visible.

Occultations have been found to be of enormous value to astronomers chiefly because study of them gives so many clues about the complex problem of a lunar atmosphere; this is especially true when a planet such as Saturn is occulted. If there happened to be any air on the Moon at all, the brightness of the planet's disc would be slightly distorted or diminished, and indeed there have been some astronomers who report observing such distortions. For an occultation of a star is of the greatest assistance not only to scientists in enabling them to check the presence of lunar atmosphere, but it also helps them to determine the Moon's exact position in the sky. It is apparent, therefore, that once our satellite's true position is known, astronomical predictions can be checked.

Opposite left: *A complete photographic sequence during a total eclipse of the Sun with multiple exposures on the same photograph. At the moment of total eclipse, in the centre, the Sun is black because it is hidden by the Moon, but the surrounding aureole of its corona is visible.*

Right: *Siamese astronomers (of the sixteenth century) observing a solar eclipse (from an ancient drawing).*

THE SUN, SOURCE OF LIFE

At a distance of 150,000,000 kilometres (93,206,000 miles) from our globe, over an abyss which light (in spite of its speed of 300,000 kilometres or 186,411 miles per second) takes eight minutes to cross, the giant Sun rules the planets. We owe our existence, the animal and plant life around us and the physical life of our planet to the energy the Sun radiates. If we can imagine the Earth without the Sun, it would be a lifeless rock lost in space.

The heat of the Sun evaporates the water of our lakes, seas and oceans, and the water vapour rises to form clouds. Over the land clouds condense and water falls as snow and rain. In the mountains hydroelectric power stations are built on the rivers to convert the flowing water into electrical energy. In this way we obtain part of the Sun's energy. This supplies factories, moves electric trains, and provides electric lights. The fuel which enables jet aircraft to speed through the skies and our cars to run on roads and highways comes from precious petroleum, a substance which originated from enormous quantities of minute organisms which lived hundreds of millions of years ago in the seas. The organisms died, were buried on the sea floor, and through the long geological periods were converted into petroleum which is stored solar energy.

When coal is burned the energy the Sun gave to the great primordial forests which covered vast areas of the Earth is released. Men long ago knew nothing about changes, such as fossilisation and chemical alteration, which have taken place during geological time; but their admiration for the Sun was nearly unlimited. The Egyptian Pharoah Akhenaton who ascended the throne about 1375 B.C. and who believed in monotheism wanted to venerate the Sun only, which was called Aton. In ancient Peru, at Cuzco, capital of the Incas, a fabulous temple was built which was dedicated to the Sun, and covered in gold leaf. Most ancient people either raised temples to the Sun or believed in elaborate solar myths. Today astronomical research enables us to understand the Sun— it is no longer mythological but more interesting and extraordinary.

The Physical Sun

The Sun's diameter measures 1,392,000 kilometres (864,949 miles) and its volume is the equivalent of 1,303,800 spheres as big as the Earth. If the Earth were placed in the heart of the Sun, then the Moon would orbit well below the Sun's surface. The Sun is much less dense than the Earth, but its mass is equal to 332,958 times the terrestrial mass. On the Sun gravity is twenty-eight times stronger than that to which we are subjected on Earth. An adult man would weigh about two tons on the Sun. Man's body could not survive the stresses to which it would be subjected by the gravitational forces of the Sun and would, therefore, be crushed literally by its own weight.

The Sun is a gigantic body of gas which is strongly condensed at the centre and incandescent at the surface. Temperature measurements of the Sun's surface reveal a heat of 6,000° C. That this is exceptionally hot can be realised when that temperature is compared with terrestrial furnaces where the temperature reaches a maximum of 1,800° C. The interior of the Sun is still hotter; it

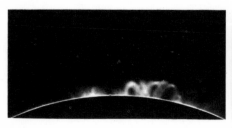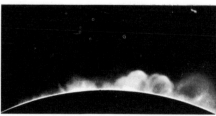

Above: *The God Ra, one of many representations of the Sun found among ancient Egyptian paintings.*
Below: *The evolution of a group of solar prominences taken through a telescope during an eclipse.*
On the following pages: *A magnificent photograph of an enormous solar prominence.*

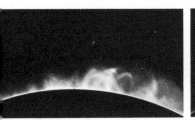 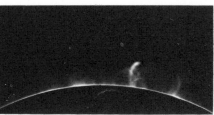 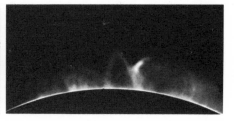

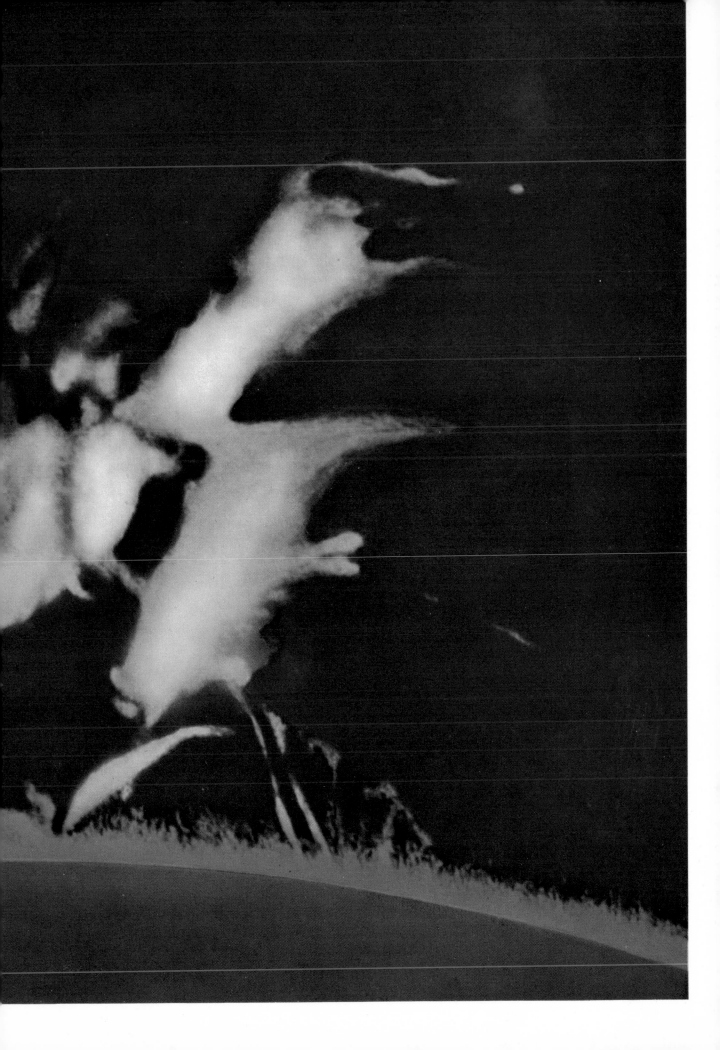

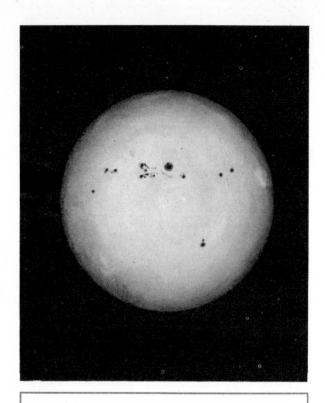

Above: *The Sun seen through a telescope during a period of intense sunspot activity. Apart from the sunspots one can see the darkening of the edge of the solar disc in which certain brighter areas stand out; these are the faculae (sun streaks).*

Below: *The electromagnetic spectrum of the Sun showing the two bands of radio and light waves which reach the terrestrial surface and are examined with optical and radio telescopes. The diagram shows the 'optical window' (to the left) and the 'radio window' (to the right).*

has been calculated that its centre reaches the incredible temperature of 35,000,000° C. Under these conditions chemical elements can exist only in the gaseous state; even at 3,000° C. iron is vapourised. The same substances which form the Earth's minerals, rocks and atmosphere, blaze in the Sun, transformed by the heat into incandescent gas.

Our knowledge of the Sun's composition is the result of a small but valuable instrument which enables scientists to make chemical analyses: the spectroscope. We have already discussed the solar spectrum which spreads its rainbow colours in the sky and which can be reproduced by using a simple prism. In the spectroscope the spectrum is enlarged and defined; and dark lines are visible—the so-called 'Fraunhofer lines', named after the Bavarian optician and physicist Joseph von Fraunhofer (1787–1826) who discovered them in the solar spectrum in 1814–1815. These lines have fixed positions in the spectrum which correspond to the light absorbed by the various elements which exist in the solar atmosphere. Each element produces its own characteristic lines which can be determined and correlated in the laboratory. Thus it is possible to analyse the Sun. In the same way, one can make an investigation of planetary atmosphere and also study the composition of extremely remote celestial bodies. The greater part of the elements known on Earth have

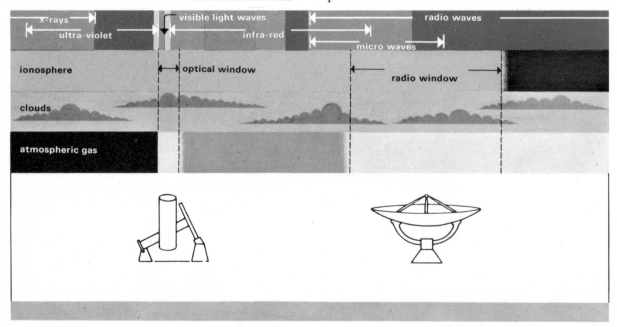

been found in the Sun. The most abundant element is hydrogen to which the fiery star owes its extraordinary physical properties.

Solar Energy

The understanding of the source of the solar energy for a long time remained one of the most provoking problems in astronomy. In ancient times it was thought that the Sun was a sphere of fire, but such a sphere would last only a few thousands of years, at the most a few tens of thousands of years. If the Sun was composed of the best quality coal it would burn for only 25,000 years, but it has radiated energy for millions and millions of years. Modern knowledge in the field of atomic physics solved the problem of the Sun's energy; this occurred in 1938 as the result of work by two astrophysicists, Hans Bethe in America and C. F. von Weizsacker in Germany. Now we know that the Sun is a gigantic nuclear fusion machine fuelled by the transformation of hydrogen into another element, helium.

In the tumultuous heart of the Sun there is a pressure equal to 100,000 million times the Earth's atmosphere and a temperature of 35,000,000° C. These conditions produce atomic reactions. The extremely high velocities with which the atoms move produce millions of collisions every second with chain reactions. As a result, every four atoms of hydrogen form one atom of helium, which weighs a little less than the four atoms from which it was created. The difference of mass is not lost but is converted into energy, which filters out from the centre until it arrives at the surface of the star, where it radiates into space in the form of light and heat, ultra-violet rays, X-rays, and radio waves. Every second, 700,000,000 tons of hydrogen are transformed into helium, liberating tremendous quantities of energy. The consumption of hydrogen is enormous, but the Sun contains so much that it can still shine for a period which has been estimated at approximately 10,000 million years.

The solar radiation forms the 'electro-magnetic spectrum' of the Sun, of which the spectrum that we see with prisms and spectroscopes is only a small part. The largest part is blocked by the atmosphere which safeguards animate objects from heavy exposure to solar radiation, in particular, the X-rays and the bulk of the ultra-violet radiation.

However, the earth's atmosphere does not filter out another equally important part of the electro-magnetic spectrum that is the radio wave region with wavelengths ranging from one centimetre to 100 metres. So we can also study the Sun from the Earth with large and powerful radio telescopes which are located in various parts of the world. When we discuss the examination of the great star with the radio telescopes which have been in regular use for the past twenty years we speak about the 'radio-sun'. Now, X-rays and ultra-violet radiation of shorter wavelength fall within the field of astronomical study. Rockets and artificial satellites suitably equipped to rise above the more absorbent layers of the atmosphere have enabled scientists to analyse them, with instruments designed to provide information in much the same way as light waves are analysed with the spectroscope.

The Photosphere

In the telescope, the Sun's blazing surface is revealed as more luminous in the centre and shaded and more attenuated towards the edge. This is the result of the absorption of its atmosphere. The visible surface, the so-called 'photosphere' (sphere of light), reveals a granular structure: the first astronomers who observed this appearance named it 'rice grains'. The grains have a diameter of about 300 kilometres (180–190 miles) and represent the tops of enormous columns of extremely hot gas, lifted and agitated continually as a result of temperature changes between the hotter and colder layers of the Sun. In places, 'faculae' are observable on the granulations as very bright areas, best seen near the edge or limb of the Sun's disc where they are prominent on the darker margin. One can clearly see the transient spots, which in certain places destroy the delicate structure of the photosphere, with the naked eye. These are the famous sunspots.

Galileo saw them first with the telescope in 1610. Almost at the same time they were seen by two other observers: the

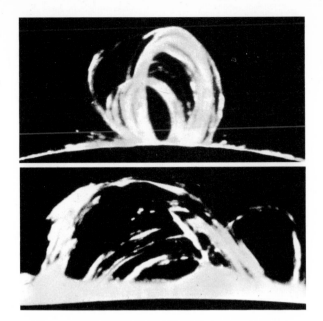

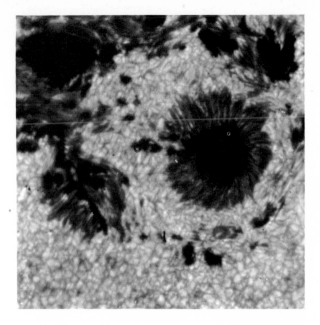

German astronomer Fr. Christoph Scheiner (1575–1650) and the Dutch astronomer David Fabricius (1564–1617). It was established from their apparent movement that the Sun rotated on its own axis. But the Sun does not have a solid crust. Therefore, at the equator its blazing gas rotates more rapidly. It has been determined that the rotation of the gas takes twenty-five days at the equator and thirty-three days in the polar zones, with all the intermediate gradations.

The photosphere appears strange because of the lack of cohesion between the poles and the equatorial belt. Relatively cold areas form in it and these are the sunspots which are probably related to disturbances in the emission or flow of energy from the internal regions of the Sun.

At first developing rapidly, variable in form and often collected in extensive groups, sunspots last for several days and even many weeks. Sunspots can be compared with gigantic turbulent crater-shaped vortices or funnels. The deepest internal parts of the spots are darkest and are called the 'umbra'. On average they are 800 kilometres (500 miles) lower than the surface of the photosphere to which they are joined by a belt which is lighter coloured and appears to consist of numerous filaments called the 'penumbra'. In these depressions the temperature is 5,000° C. The temperature drop of 1000° C. from the surrounding zone creates turbulence of an intensity that is

Above left: *Two successive photographs of a great solar prominence in active development.*

Above right: *An impressive picture of the turbulent solar photosphere taken in September 1957 from a telescope mounted on a balloon.*

Opposite page: *The outer layers of the radiant Sun as revealed by astronomical observations. At the bottom, the photosphere can be seen with its granulations and its tumultuous depressions, the sunspots. Above the photosphere is the chromosphere from which the prominences erupt.*

nearly impossible to imagine. The Earth, apart from being vapourised in such extreme temperatures, would be swept away like a leaf in a hurricane. A few sunspots have been observed which have extended over a length of 300,000 kilometres (186,500 miles)— that is almost equal to the distance from the Earth to the Moon.

Near the spots, and always in the zone of the faculae, sudden increases in luminosity sometimes are produced which last for a few minutes and then slowly die out. These are solar flares produced by tremendous explosions of energy, which are resolved in hydrogen eruptions at extremely high temperatures. Since the sunspots are centres of intense magnetic fields, the flares are phenomena bound to the magnetic activity of the Sun. The wave of disturbance generated travels over the solar surface at a velocity of 1,000 kilometres per second (625 miles per second). It is difficult to appreciate the enormous

73

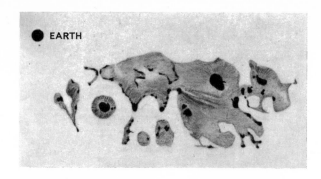

EARTH

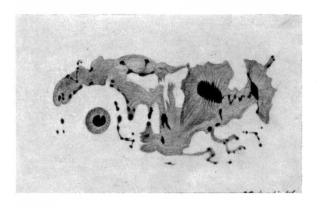

Phenomena of gigantic intensity occur in the sunspots. The two black-and-white pictures above *show the changes observed in a large group of sunspots in July 1946*: top, *as they appeared on 26 July*; below, *on 29 July*.

Bottom of the page: *This sequence of photographs showing the displacement of the sunspots on the solar disc reveals the rotation of the Sun on its axis.*

Opposite page: *The solar corona photographed during the total eclipse, 15 February 1961.*

scale of the endless phenomena which affect the Sun in such a variety of ways.

The Chromosphere and the Corona

The solar atmosphere vanishes into space through two envelopes, which become more

and more tenuous: the chromosphere and the corona. Principally composed of hydrogen and helium, the chromosphere (sphere of colour) gives off a marvellous red-pink light, but its transparency above the blazing photosphere renders it completely invisible. It is studied, however, every day: with the spectroscope, or its photographic application, the spectroheliograph, and with an interference filter, an instrument recently created by the French astronomer Bernard Ferdinand Lyot (d. 1952).

In the past we could admire the chromosphere's beauty only in the rare moments of a total eclipse of the Sun. The chromosphere is completely irregular with thin palpitating points. From the bulk of it, gigantic flames of hydrogen and calcium are emitted. These are the 'prominences' which are formed in the shape of fountains, plumes, branching trees and cloudy piles. They rise from the Sun with a velocity of hundreds of kilometres (hundreds of miles) per second, and they break up in space only to fall back on to the great star. They would reduce the Earth to vapour in a moment if it were in their paths. In 1919 a solar prominence was observed which extended for more than 800,000 kilometres (500,000 miles above the photosphere: this is more than twice the distance from the Earth to the Moon.

Farther out, the corona projects around the Sun a marvellous aureole of plumes which are yellow internally and suffused with the tints of mother-of-pearl on the outside. Only an eclipse gives us a complete view of the corona. The coronagraph, also developed by Lyot, enables us to make daily studies of its deeper parts where the prodigious jets of the prominences

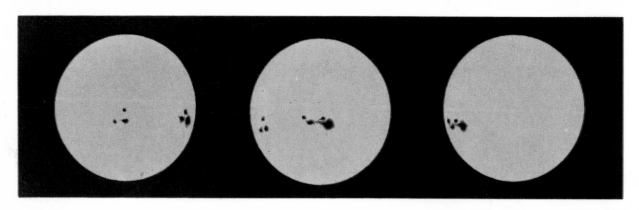

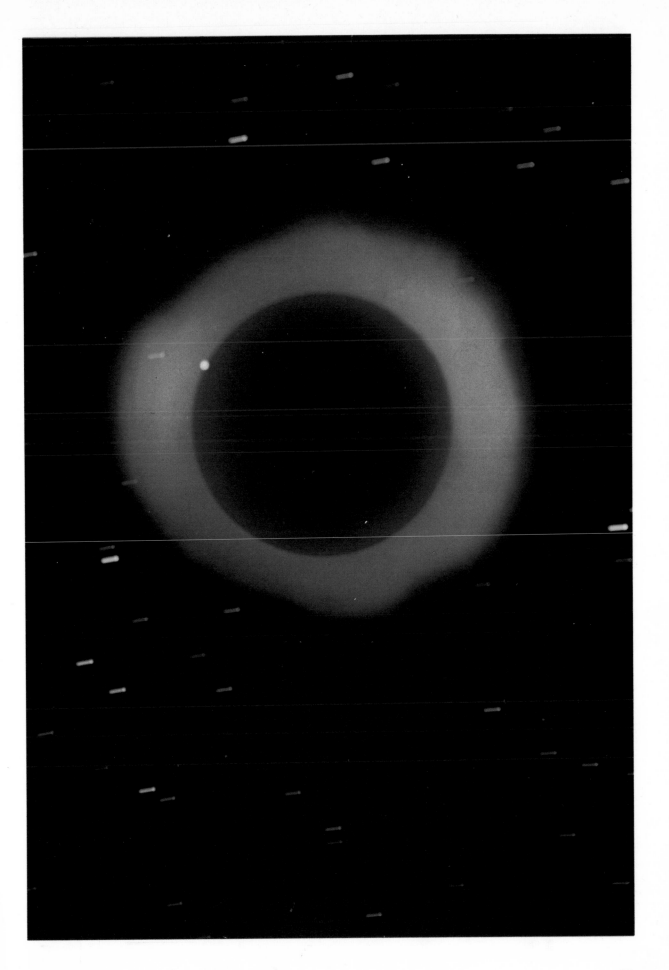

emerge. The corona is very tenuous, even the most fragile comets can pass through it without the slightest disturbance of their motion, and yet it produces clearly defined plumes up to 25,000,000 kilometres (15,534,000 miles) from the Sun.

All these prodigious phenomena—sunspots, solar flares, prominences, and coronal plumes—have a rhythmical cycle which lasts on average eleven years. During active periods of the eleven-year solar cycle, there is a maximum in both the number and activity of the sunspots, flares and prominences, and the corona assumes certain shapes not seen at other times. On the other hand, during the quiet periods, months pass without the appearance of sunspots, and other phenomena such as the corona are very different in appearance.

In 1957 and 1958 groups of scientists from all parts of the world undertook a series of observations of a geophysical nature, among which were investigations of the Sun's activity. This enterprise was called the International Geophysical Year (I.G.Y.). During the period, solar activity was at a maximum and the study of this activity was an important part of the programme.

Again, in 1964 and 1965, a similar programme was arranged which was called the International Quiet Sun Years (I.Q.S.Y.). As a result of new instruments and new techniques these two co-ordinated international programmes have provided a wealth of information which is still being studied. Probably one of the most important results of the studies is our improved knowledge of the effect solar radiation has on work in telecommunications.

The physical life of the Earth is affected by all the changes in the solar rhythm. When the flares, inexhaustible fountains of X-rays, ultra-violet rays, radio waves and jets of particles explode, all the terrestrial conditions change: the magnetic field varies considerably, the ionosphere is modified and influences radio transmission, and the equilibrium of the entire terrestrial atmosphere is affected. When the jets of particles arrive (between twenty-two and thirty-four hours after the hydrogen eruptions) magnetic storms burst on the planet, and in the skies of the polar zones the marvellous auroral lights appear. There can be no doubt that these are the most impressive phenomena and, therefore, the most easily observable and measurable; but who can say to what extent the terrestrial equilibrium and even man's own delicate physical equilibrium is affected by what happens in the Sun?

The internal part of the Solar System is shown here on the same scale as two types of stars which will be discussed later: a blue giant and a red super giant.

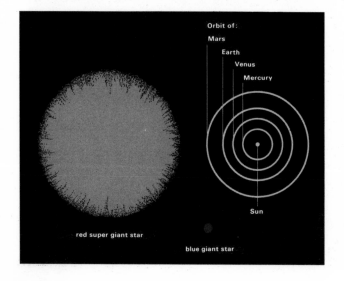

Orbit of:
Mars
Earth
Venus
Mercury

Sun

red super giant star

blue giant star

Part Three

THE SOLAR SYSTEM

PLANETS AND SATELLITES

Every night, after the violet-coloured mists of evening are extinguished in the west, the constellations unfold over our heads and outline unchangeable shapes in the sky. Against this background certain celestial bodies move continually. These are among the brightest in the firmament, propelled by uninterrupted motion which makes them move in front of the motionless constellations. The ancient Greeks took the name planet from the word *planetai* which means 'vagrant'. Today we know that these small points of light form a family of worlds which orbit the Sun in the same way as Earth does.

The planets are cold dark globes; they shine with the reflected light from the Sun which sometimes makes them appear as bright as celestial diamonds. Because the planets are separated from us by enormous distances we are not fully aware of their real appearance, which is hidden to the naked eye. However, the telescope reveals them as spheres and at least enables us to see the essential characteristics which give their surfaces variable features.

The planets are seen as quite small discs. Even those with the largest diameter appear about forty times smaller than the Moon in the largest telescopes. When we observe the planets we can only see their broader surface features although astronomers know that they must be made up of smaller details.

The study of the planets, some of which in the last few years have become the goal for journeys into space, is one of astronomy's most fascinating subjects. Without the telescope man can see only five of the worlds which comprise the Sun's dominion. These are the planets noted by the ancient astronomers: Mercury, Venus, Mars, Jupiter and Saturn. Together with the Sun and the Moon, for thousands of years, they have represented for man the mobile stars as compared with the immutable firmament or the 'heaven of the fixed stars'.

During the last two centuries, the number of worlds has been increased by the discovery of numerous celestial bodies which follow the Sun and are held by its gravitational attraction: Uranus, Neptune, Pluto and a myriad of minor planets, or asteroids. It has been discovered that the pale comets, although very different from the bright planets, are slaves of the Sun, too, as are the meteors, fragments of worlds which reach Earth's surface as meteorites. The Sun's family is very extensive and extremely varied. This complex of other worlds, of vagrant faint lights, and small fragments is called the Solar System.

The Earth is as much a part of the Solar System as are the most gigantic bodies and the microscopic meteors. But in past centuries, this fact was not evident. The Earth had been placed at the centre of the universe and so the Moon, Sun and the other

Above: *A diagram showing the planets which compose the Solar System all drawn to scale.*

Opposite page: *The great Polish astronomer Nicholas Copernicus (1473-1543) receiving the first printed copy of his* De revolutionibus orbium coelestium *a short time before his death.*

planets had to move around it. We have already mentioned that the ancient Greeks quickly conceived the idea of a spherical Earth: from this knowledge they derived the idea of other external transparent spheres, which enveloped the globe and to which the various celestial bodies were attached. The movements of these spheres, in which the heavenly bodies were fixed, had different velocities which explained the movements seen in the sky. In this way, the ancient Greeks arrived at an explanation of the entire universe in which the Earth was not only immobile but did not even rotate on its axis.

The gigantic crystalline spheres were thought to exist inside an enormous hollow sphere of fixed stars. The Greeks thought that each of these spheres produced a different sound. The fusion of these sounds would thus create marvellous harmony—'the music of the spheres'—but the ears of men, being accustomed to the sound, could no longer hear it.

In order to explain all the movements of the heavenly bodies Eudoxus of Cnidus (408–355 B.C.) imagined a complicated system of twenty-seven spheres. A little later Aristotle (384–322 B.C.) increased this number to fifty-two.

It is a remarkable fact that at the time that the idea of the hollow spheres prevailed,

there were a few isolated intuitions of reality. Aristarchus of Samos (280–264 B.C.) affirmed that all the planets rotated around the Sun and that the Earth itself was one of the planets. Aristarchus's arguments were ignored, and fell into oblivion for nearly two thousand years. The idea of a universe with the fixed Earth at the centre remained dominant.

Later, from the idea of musical spheres, man passed to a belief in a system of circles definitely established by a famous astronomer and geographer from Alexandria, Egypt, Claudius Ptolemy, who, in the second

Below left: *A mechanical device to illustrate the Copernican concept of the cosmos. The raised points represent the Sun and the planets.*

Below right: *Ptolemy's sphere: a seventeenth century artistic design showing the universe, with the Earth at the centre.*

SPHERE DE PTOLEMÉE

century A.D., wrote a classical text called *The Almagest*. It seemed then that accurate knowledge of the heavens had been finally acquired and the so-called 'Ptolemaic system' dominated the science of astronomy for more than a thousand years.

Dante, in the *Divine Comedy* (1308–9), described his ascent to the Empyrean (the highest heaven) through the heavens of the various planets (arranged concentrically around the Earth) from the one near the Moon to the final remote one of Saturn enclosed in the unchanging firmament. This was the Ptolemaic system presented in the greatest of the poems. Over two hundred years later, in 1543, a book which revolutionised astronomy appeared; it placed the Sun at the centre of the group of planets which included the Earth. The book was the *De revolutionibus orbium coelestium* by Nicholas Copernicus, who was born at Thorn in Poland in 1473. The rotating immaterial heavens, or the crystalline spheres, yielded their place to the reality of the Solar System. With the publication of Copernicus's ideas modern astronomy was born.

In the Copernican system only the Moon revolved around the Earth; the Earth and the other planets all revolved around the Sun. Copernicus also supposed, as did Ptolemy, that the planets moved in circular orbits, but Johann Kepler established the orbits' elliptical form. Tycho Brahe, the astronomer mentioned earlier whose precise observations were utilised by Kepler, postulated a system in 1582 in which the planets revolved around the Sun, but the Sun itself with its followers revolved around the immobile Earth.

The Tycho system was of brief duration; thirty years later, Galileo's observations brought the first incontestable proof of the Copernican system.

Below left: *Claudius Ptolemy who proposed the system which bears his name.*
Below right: *The Copernican sphere: similar to the sphere on the previous page, but with the Sun at the centre and the planets rotating around it.*

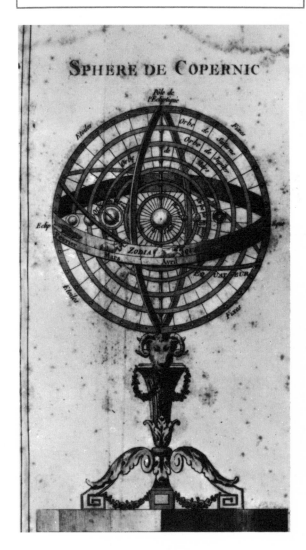

THE WORLDS BETWEEN THE EARTH AND THE SUN

One of the fundamental objections of people opposed to Copernicus's system was: if Mercury and Venus rotate in their orbits between the Earth and the Sun, they must present phases like the Moon. In fact, they do not. The argument that the great distances involved hid the observation of these phases was not considered valid. As soon as Galileo turned his telescope to Venus, the dazzling planet appeared as a crescent-like tiny Moon. Twenty-five years later, with the help of more powerful telescopes than those used by Galileo, it was seen that Mercury had the same appearance.

It is easy to understand how the two planets which revolve within the terrestrial orbit cannot reveal a completely illuminated hemisphere except in particular circumstances. When they are on the same side of Earth as the Sun they are invisible, as is the New Moon. And, like the Moon, they can pass in front of the Sun's disc, although they only produce small eclipses visible with a telescope. When Mercury and Venus are transported by their motion away from the Sun, they appear as thin crescents which gradually increase in size until they become complete discs. But when the completely illuminated disc of the Sun is turned towards us, then both Mercury and Venus disappear in its brilliant aureole. Emerging from the Sun's rays, they repeat their phases inversely until they turn their darkened hemisphere towards us. When they reach a point closest to the Earth, the examination of their surfaces becomes impossible. It is much more difficult to study Mercury and Venus than the planets outside the terrestrial orbit like Mars and Jupiter.

The Earth is the third planet in order of distance from the Sun in the Solar System. The nearest to the central star is Mercury, followed by Venus. The fourth in order is Mars, beyond which the minor planets, or asteroids, orbit. Farther still, are the giants of the system: Jupiter, Saturn, Uranus and Neptune. Pluto is the last of the planetary worlds.

Among all these bodies, only Mercury and Venus can appear as crescents like the Moon. Their appearance in the telescope is, therefore, not only unusual but very fascinating. When Venus's phase is marked, a modest telescope will reveal its thin crescent which

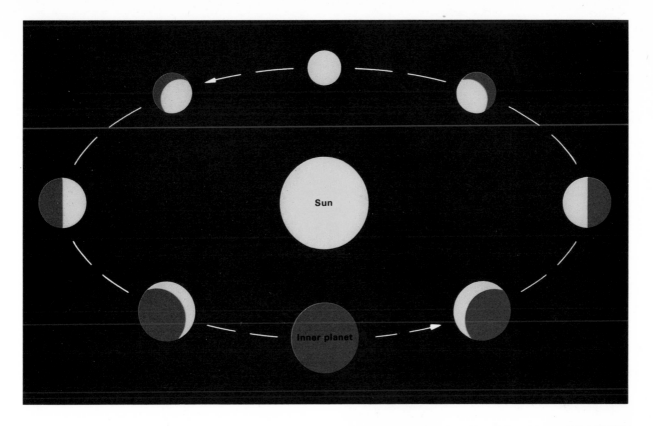

shines with the brilliance of a diamond. Under the most favourable conditions, even a good pair of binoculars can reveal Venus as a miniature version of our Moon.

Mercury

Of the planets within the Earth's orbit the first, Mercury, is also the smallest. Its diameter is only 4,800 kilometres (about 3,000

Above: *A diagram showing how the phases of the inner group of planets are produced, depending on their variable positions relative to the Sun. As a result of these phases, Mercury and Venus repeat the various appearances of the Moon when seen through the telescope.*

Below: *The ancient Greek gods which lived on Mount Olympus.*

miles) and its mass is equivalent to fifty-four thousandths of that of the Earth. Mercury is a planet similar in size to the Moon. Like the Moon, it does not have an enveloping atmosphere because it has very weak gravity. But the similarity between Mercury and our satellite does not end there: Mercury reflects the sunlight from a rough surface like our Moon. The landscapes of the Moon and Mercury are probably very similar. The surface of Mercury seems to be very rugged and there are rather large grey patches which, in the telescope, appear to be similar to the Moon's so-called seas. Another similarity between the two, is the lack of water. Water could not possibly exist in a liquid state on the side of Mercury nearest the Sun. And, because of Mercury's very thin atmosphere, water could not even exist as vapour.

At an average distance of 58,000,000 kilometres (36,000,000 miles) from the Sun, the small planet completes its orbit in eighty-eight days, which is the length of its year. Since it is only a short distance from the Sun in the sky, it is seen with difficulty at intervals of a few weeks as a reddish point of light in the morning or evening.

The study of Mercury through the telescope is difficult because of its proximity to the Sun's rays and its great distance from the Earth together with the inconvenience of its phases. On its disc, which appears incomplete because of its darkened hemisphere, one can see faint brown markings on a copper-coloured background. Even the most powerful optical instruments do not reveal mountains or craters in these markings, so the geography of Mercury is less well known than that of the Moon.

A century ago it was thought that Mercury rotated on its axis in a period more or less equal to that of the Earth and that, therefore, the days and nights were as long as on Earth. Then the Italian astronomer Giovanni V. Schiaparelli (1835–1910) speculated that the planet always presented the same side to the Sun, as the Moon does to the Earth. In relation to the stars, the orbital period of eighty-eight days found by Schiaparelli was corrected in 1968 to fifty-nine days as a result of radio astronomical observations at Arecibo, Puerto Rico. In respect to the Sun, Mercury's orbit is one hundred and seventy-six days, and it is subjected to very slow alternation of light and darkness.

Because it is so close to the Sun, the little planet receives radiation seven times more intense on its surface than the Earth receives, and there is no filtering atmosphere. On its illuminated surface, direct measurements have revealed temperatures in excess of 400° C. (752° F.) which are capable of melting lead. The temperature on its darkened side must be almost at absolute zero, which is more than 250° C. (482° F.) below zero. With days which last about three months, and equally long nights, there is an alternation of these extreme temperatures which is unimaginable to us. An endless night on Mercury, as cold as that on the most remote planet, Pluto, follows a day with the Sun blazing in a sky made black because there is no atmosphere. Life as we know it under these conditions is impossible.

Venus

Moving away from the Sun, across the Solar System, beyond the desolation of Mercury, the mysterious planet, Venus, is encountered. Even though no other planet comes so close to the Earth (its minimum distance is 42,000,000 kilometres or 26,100,000 miles), Venus remains one of the most enigmatic of the heavenly bodies because of the dense layer of clouds which envelopes it and perpetually obscures its surface. Mercury and the Moon, with their bare rocky surfaces exposed to the Sun's rays, reflect seven per cent of the light they receive from the Sun; however, the clouds of Venus reflect fifty-nine per cent of the Sun's light. The planet's secrets are hidden under this planet's mantle which makes it one of the most beautiful bodies in the sky.

Venus's diameter measures 12,310 kilometres (7,649 miles), and its mass is eight-tenths of that of our planet; it is, therefore, almost a twin sister of the Earth, but just a little smaller. It completes its orbit in two hundred and twenty-five days at an average distance (radius) of 108,000,000 kilometres (67,100,000 miles) from the Sun. In the telescope, during its splendid phases, vague dark areas are observable between the brighter zones. These areas were once thought to be continents and oceans, but they are actually the result of the variations in density and transparency of the cloudy mantle, and not a part of the planet's surface. Many astronomers have attempted to confirm the appearance of various feature's of Venus's surface. But so far, there have been no conclusive discoveries. Venus's atmosphere is such that the shadings and light patches which can be seen in telescopic observations are almost certainly the planet's heavy cloud layers.

In 1728, the Italian Francesco Bianchini (1662–1729) concluded that Venus rotated once in twenty-four days and eight hours.

Above: *Venus seen through the telescope.*

Right: *Drawings of Venus made by the Italian astronomer Francesco Bianchini in 1726.*

Below: *Since Venus has a dense atmosphere and the Moon lacks one they present different appearances when they exhibit the same phase. Fig. a: the Moon seen with the naked eye. Fig. b: Venus seen through the telescope. The atmosphere of Venus prolongs the ends of the thin crescent of the planet. Fig. c: when Venus is near the Sun, the diffused light in its atmosphere shows as a very thin luminous ring.*

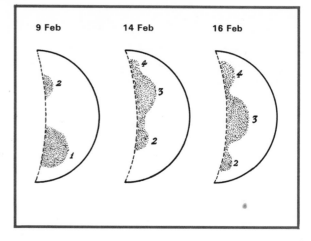

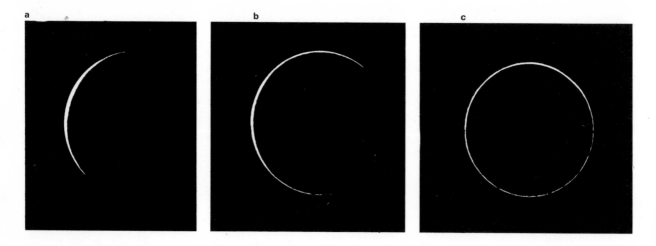

He observed the marks on Venus with a telescope which was thirty metres (exactly 100 feet) long, and he drew a map of the geography of the neighbouring planet which was considered an accurate representation for more than a century. However, in 1890, Schiaparelli observed that Venus always turned the same hemisphere towards the Sun, which meant that its rotation was equal to the length of its year or two hundred and twenty-five days. In 1964, Schiaparelli's results were corrected to two hundred and forty-seven days. Now, radar has established that Venus rotates clockwise once every two hundred and forty-three days. All other planets rotate counterclockwise.

In 1761 the Russian astronomer Mikhail Lomonosov (1711–1765) observed the passage of Venus in front of the Sun and saw the planet's dark disc surrounded by a ring of light from which he deduced the presence of an atmospheric envelope diffusing the Sun's rays. This prolongs the points of the crescent Venus and sometimes reveals the planet as a brilliant thin ring even when it does not pass directly in front of the Sun. It has been calculated that the pressure of Venus's atmosphere at the planet's surface is more than ten times that to which the Earth is subjected, and that the clouds which we observe extend from 70 kilometres (44 miles) above the surface to a height of 100 kilometres (62 miles). It has been discovered that these clouds contain great quantities of carbon dioxide; and recently the presence of water vapour has been confirmed. The brilliant clouds are certainly composed in part of ice crystals or droplets of water, but their total composition still remains unknown.

The *Venus* and *Mariner* probes have approached the bright planet. The U.S. probe, *Venus III* (March 1966), and the Russian probe, *Venera IV* (October 1967), even reached the planet's surface. *Mariner II* (U.S.) recordings, based on studies of microwave frequencies, gave a calculated ground or surface temperature of 327° C. (620° F.) But *Venera IV* recorded temperatures ranging from 40° to 280° C. (104° to 536° F.). The Russian probe also recorded a pressure profile of from one to fifteen atmospheres during its parachute descent to the surface. Results of the U.S. *Mariner V* probe, which passed within 2,500 miles of Venus, will provide even more data.

A 'sea of clouds', which can be seen from the tops of mountains, shows how difficult it is to study the surface of Venus which is hidden by clouds.

MYSTERIOUS MARS

The Living Planet

In the heart of pink and red Martian deserts, the broken edges of craters are open to the sky which is deep indigo in colour. In the cold tenuous atmosphere the Sun's rays evaporate the thin film of frost which is deposited during the cold nights on the higher hills, on the plateaux and on the crags which emerge from the sand. The movement of the air which becomes warmer raises the fine dust which covers the rocks and gravel with a thin film, dragging yellow mists against the hills of the clear countryside. The colour of its deserts clothes Mars with a red light which made the ancient Greeks call it *Pyrois* (burning). Our description is obtained from the most recent research and is the way Mars, the living planet, looks today.

Mars, of all the planets in the Solar System, is the one which astronomers and scientists know most about. Although Mars never comes as close to the Earth as does Venus, for example, when the red planet is nearest we can observe its fully illuminated disc, whereas Venus is obscured by cloud layers.

Outside the Earth's orbit, Mars circles around the Sun at an average distance of 228,000,000 kilometres (141,673,000 miles) accompanied by its small moons, Phobos and Deimos, with diameters of a few kilometres each. Mars completes its orbit in six hundred and eighty-seven days. Mars's diameter is only 6,790 kilometres (4,219 miles) and its mass is about one-tenth of that of the Earth. As a result of its weak gravity it retains only a very thin atmosphere. After receiving data from the space probe *Mariner IV* in 1965 scientists determined that the density at Mars's surface is only one-hundredth part of ours.

The Martian atmosphere is composed mainly of nitrogen like that of the Earth. Carbon dioxide has been discovered in Mars's atmosphere and water vapour, in very small quantities, has also been recorded. If this vapour were condensed to form water on the planet's surface it would probably form a layer less than one millimetre thick. Therefore, on Mars it never rains and the cumulus clouds which bring storms to the Earth do not form in the sky. There are only evening mists, nocturnal frosts and tenuous clouds of ice crystals, which are similar to our cirrus clouds. It seems certain that fine crystals of ice form a transparent layer over all the planet. This is the 'blue layer' of Mars, so-called because of its appearance when photographed in blue or violet light. Because of

Below: *Various aspects of the planet Mars seen during successive observations on the same night.*

Opposite page: *Photographs of Mars with the relative maps giving the names of the shapes illustrated.*

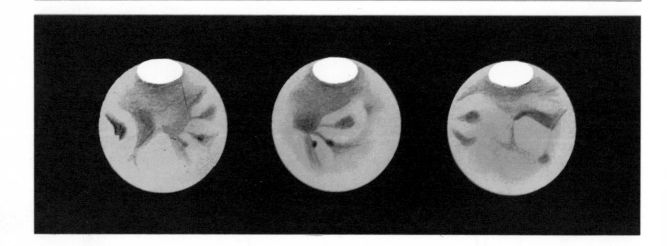

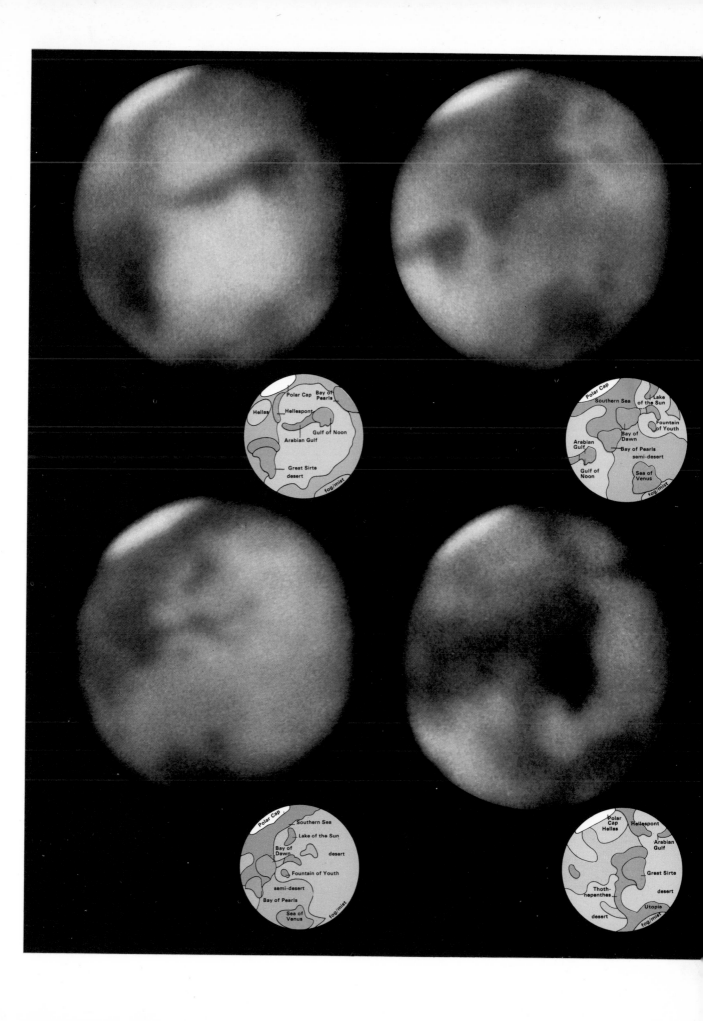

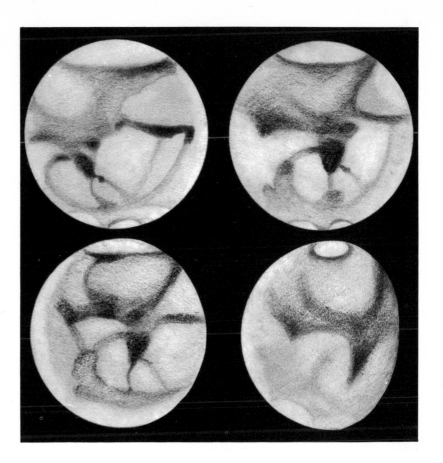

Left: *The sands of the Sahara photographed from the capsule* Gemini 11 *in September 1966. The Martian deserts are comparable to Earth's coloured deserts.*

Right: *Mars observed through the telescope over a period of about four months. The views were taken on the 8th of June 1954* (top left), *the 13th of June 1954* (top right), *20th of July 1954* (bottom left) *and 30th of September 1954* (bottom right). *One can see the great seasonal changes: the restriction of the southern polar cap (at the top edge of the disc) and the darkening of marks on the southern hemisphere (clearly seen when one compares the two left-hand views).*

the lack of water, there are no oceans and seas.

Oxygen has not been found in the atmosphere of Mars. If the primeval Martian atmosphere contained any oxygen this has probably been largely eliminated from it by the process of oxidation. This means that the oxygen has combined with minerals in the rocks of the Martian crust. This fact demonstrates the fundamental difference between the Martian environment and that of the Earth. *Mariner IV* established another difference: the globe of Mars is non-magnetic and therefore is not surrounded by the protective Van Allen belts. We do not fully understand, as yet, up to what point the thin atmosphere of Mars can compensate for this lack of protection. There are valid reasons for believing that it can provide a shield against the radiation and particles coming from outer space sufficient to sustain life.

Mars rotates on its axis in twenty-four hours and thirty-seven minutes; therefore its days and nights are about as long as ours. Another surprising similarity is that Mars's axis of rotation is inclined at an angle of 25° to the perpendicular with the plane of its orbit; this is almost the same as that of the Earth relative to the plane of the ecliptic. There are, therefore, seasons on the planet like ours, but these last twice as long and the climatic conditions are much more severe.

In the dark marks of the planet, the temperature near the equator just after midday is only 10° C. (50° F.) and can reach a maximum, in limited areas, of 25–30° C. (77–86° F.). At sunset in the same areas the temperature falls well below zero. The red deserts are much colder, around zero° C. (32°F.) depending on locality. These deserts may have a greater overall altitude than the dark areas.

In a manner similar to the other planets the distance from the Earth to Mars varies continually as a result of the positions occupied by the two bodies in their orbits. When Mars is exactly opposite the Sun (a similar condition to that of the Full Moon), it oscillates between 99,000,000 and 56,000,000 kilometres (61,500,000 and 35,000,000 miles). The nearest approach at 56,000,000 kilometres occurs every fifteen to seventeen

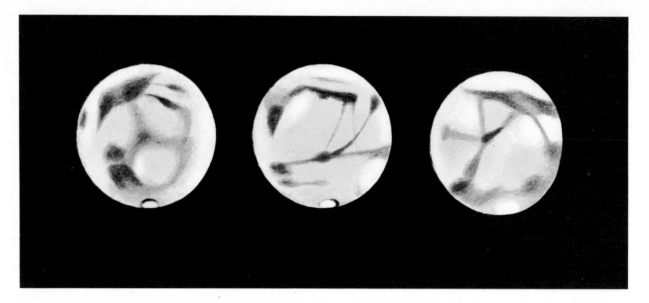

years and takes the name of the 'great oppositions'. For example, great oppositions have occurred, or will occur in 1956, 1971, and 1988. On these occasions all available astronomical facilities are used to gain more information about the red planet.

Under favourable conditions Mars offers a fine sight when seen through the telescope. Its reddish disc, with brick-red or copper-coloured zones fades towards the edge into yellow—a colour produced by dust raised by the winds. On this background the marks stand out prominently. They are generally blue-green and seem to form an outline of seas with gulfs, inlets and straits. We know, however, that these marks cannot be real seas because of the lack of water which was mentioned earlier.

Above: *Views of Mars with the arctic polar cap visible (taken during the opposition of 1952 when the planet was close to the Earth, the cap is seen at the bottom). The marks on the southern regions appear deformed compared with the preceding pictures because they were seen from a different point of view.*

Bottom left: *Mars during the great opposition of 1956; (the night of 19 August). On the disc the Sun Lake (Lacus Solis) on the left, and the Sea of Syrens (Mare Sireum) on the right, can be seen. At the top the southern polar cap is in an advanced state of dissolution.*

Bottom right: *Another view of Mars in 1956 (16 August). One can see the retreat of the southern polar cap better here. (All observations on this page were made by Guido Ruggieri.)*

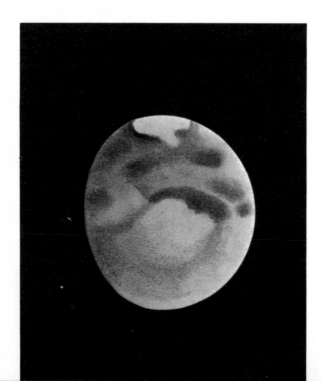

The Surface of the Red Planet

The dark marks on Mars do not remain immobile like those that trace the face of our Moon. Because of the diurnal rotation of the planet, they move slowly across the disc which appears in the eyepiece of the telescope. We see the dark marks slowly rise at the edge of the disc, then move to the central meridian and finally disappear at the opposite edge.

On each pole brilliant white caps shine, which the transparent Martian atmosphere colours light blue. The Earth's poles have similar but much more extensive caps.

If prolonged observations are made for weeks or months, surprising changes in the planet are seen. The brilliant polar caps shrink in size alternately following the seasonal rhythm. While on one hemisphere, in the autumn, the cap reappears under pale wisps of mist, on the other hemisphere advancing spring erodes the white cap surrounding the end of the rotational axis and slowly reduces it until summer transforms it into a tiny bright fragment or it disappears completely. In spring from the diminishing cap a dark wave spreads and invades the 'seas' stretching them towards the opposite pole. After this there is another more extraordinary phase: from the cap, by this time reduced in size, a brown wave moves towards the equator overriding the 'seas' and giving them variable shades which range from red to violet. This wave even travels as far as the other pole. Each season brings these periodical changes to the Martian hemispheres. Only scientists who have followed these changes directly through the telescope can form an adequate idea of the great cycle which occurs on the red planet, making it a living world—at least from the point of view of its physical environment.

The more or less complete disappearance of the caps should not be surprising. The scarcity of water implies that these caps are certainly not great thicknesses of ice like those that cover the terrestrial Arctic or Antarctic. The Martian polar caps are thin deposits of powdery snow, only a few centimetres—perhaps only a few millimetres—thick which evaporate directly into the extremely dry atmosphere without forming water. The humidity which is liberated is dispersed through the atmosphere towards the equator and darkens the bluish marks. It is clear that the cycle of these marks depends on the water vapour which is released by the caps.

What exactly are these dark areas that respond to the humidity and change with a seasonal rhythm? The intense research on various parts of the planet has proved that the red or rose-coloured zones reflect the light as do some terrestrial rocks and dust deposits. The dark marks reflect light not as rocks do but like mosses or dry lichens or layers of microscopic algae. Therefore, it is entirely probable that on Mars, in the lower and warmer areas, organic life, at least plant life, occurs at the level of the simplest organisms. Whatever other hypotheses about the dark areas are presented, none satisfy scientific observations so well. Under laboratory conditions which reproduce the Martian environment, algae, protozoa and small arthropoda generally survive and sometimes can even reproduce.

The geography of Mars thus assumes a particular fascination. In the recent past it was thought that there were indications of more advanced life on Mars. During the great opposition of 1877, the astronomer Schiaparelli, saw a certain number of dark thin lines linking the dark marks across the reddish areas. He called the bluish areas 'seas' and baptised them with ancient and legendary geographical names. He also called the lines 'canals'. These lines were soon discovered by other astronomers, who considered them artificial and supposed that water flowed through them.

Do 'Martians' Really Exist?

At the end of the nineteenth century, the American astronomer Percival Lowell (d. 1916) made a special study of the 'canals' and discovered an enormous number of thin ones. He openly declared that these were *real* irrigation canals constructed by the inhabitants of Mars to sustain life on their almost desiccated planet. As a result of his research, the term 'Martians' arose and their cities were thought to exist in the heart of the red deserts. More accurate observations

demonstrated that the canals were not true lines, but accumulations of minute particles disposed along certain lines controlled by the superficial structure of the planet. An important detailed study of this subject was made by the Greek astronomer E. M. Antoniadi who worked in Paris, with the largest telescope in Europe, during the important oppositions of 1909 and 1924. In 1923, he prepared a map of Mars which is the most detailed in existence. Antoniadi's conclusions were confirmed, in general, by Gerard Peter Kuiper in America in 1956 using the great telescope of the McDonald Observatory in Texas. However, these views have not been universally accepted. The controversy about the true nature of the surface of Mars will no doubt continue until man actually sets foot upon the planet and is able to explain the appearance of 'canals'.

Ideas about Martians, their cities and enormous irrigation works have gradually disappeared, and research scientists are now trying to resolve the mysteries of the changeable dark marks. The possibility that there are 'living' Martians will be explored by a special probe which will land on the planet and transmit positive data on the subject. This Mars probe is called 'Project Gulliver', and its realisation is perhaps not too distant.

In the meantime, the study of Mars with space probes has begun. *Mariner IV* photographed the craters, comparable with those of the Moon, which cover the surface of our neighbouring world and which no one thought existed. It has been calculated that there are at least 10,000 craters on the entire planet. Their origin presents the same problems that we must resolve for Earth's satellite, the Moon.

Martian Satellites

Mars's two satellites are only visible with very powerful telescopes. They were first discovered in 1877 by Asaph Hall using a large refractor at Washington Observatory. Because Mars is a dazzlingly brilliant planet, the two faint lights of the satellites are usually hard to distinguish.

Phobos revolves at about 3,700 miles above the surface of Mars and Deimos circles at about 12,500 miles. Phobos completes a revolution around Mars in seven hours and thirty-nine minutes, while Deimos takes thirty hours and eighteen minutes.

Astronomers do not have any idea of what the surface of these satellites is like because they only appear as points of light in telescopes. Scientists have attempted to estimate their size by studying their relative brightness. Phobos seems to have a diameter of about ten miles and Deimos seems to have a five mile diameter. This means that neither satellite is bigger than a largish city on Earth and both would fit in London's boundaries.

AONIUS SINUS
THYLE I
MARE CHRONIUM
ERIDANIA
ELECTRIS
SIMOS
THAUMASIA
PHAETONTIS
(PHAETHONTIS)
PHASIS
BATHYS
SOLIS LACUS
MARE CIMMERIUM
MARE SIRENUM
ACAMPSIS
SIRENUM SINUS
ATLANTIS
MEMNONIA
ELISON
EOSPHORES
ARAXES
LACUS PHOENICIS
IRIS
EUMENIDES
DAEDALIA
SIRENIUS
ZEPHYRIA
ZEPHYRIA
TARTARUS
TRIANGLE
THARSIS
ARSIA SILVA
NODUS GORDI
EUMENIDES
ULYSSES
ORCUS
GIGAS
AMAZONIS
HOUGERIUS LACUS
ALBIS LACUS
NIX OLYMPICA

THE ASTEROIDS AND COLOSSAL JUPITER

The Minor Planets

Beyond Mars, between its orbit and that of giant Jupiter, there is an abyss of 550,000,000 kilometres (342,000,000 miles). Almost two centuries after the invention of the telescope, scientists still believed that the abyss was empty. Now we know that the abyss is populated by a swarm of very small bodies, the minor planets or asteroids, which because of their size could not be seen by either the naked eye or the telescope. The largest of these appear no bigger than luminous points even with the best telescopic instruments.

In 1801, the year in which the first asteroid was discovered, about two thousand altogether were discovered. It is not possible to be absolutely accurate about the number of asteroids and other bodies which exist between Mars and Jupiter, but it has been calculated that the Mount Wilson telescope would enable about 45,000 to be seen. In fact, asteroids are so numerous that astronomers call them the 'vermin of the skies'.

The largest body, Ceres, which was the first to be discovered, has a diameter of 770 kilometres (478 miles). The second to be discovered, Pallas, is no greater than 490 kilometres (304 miles) in diameter. Another ten or so exceed at the most only 100 kilometres (62 miles) in diameter. The remaining number, almost all the swarm, comprise smaller bodies, which are not even globes but irregular rock masses. The giants of the group are similar to the Moon, but much more irregular. On these orbiting bodies there is no atmosphere, no physical phenomena, and probably not the slightest trace of life. The band of minor planets is nothing more than a desert of rocky debris scattered throughout empty space.

The asteroids are controlled by the laws of gravitation and almost all describe their orbits between Mars and Jupiter. A few move outside that zone and create strange irregularities in the Solar System. While the asteroid Hidalgo, with a flattened orbit, moves at its aphelion beyond remote Saturn,

The giant planet Jupiter as it appears through the telescope. At the right one of the four major moons can be seen while it passes in front of the planet's disc casting a small shadow.

Opposite page: Galileo, in his villa at Arcetri, near Florence, Italy, showing Jupiter's moons and the other marvels he discovered in the heavens to the great English poet John Milton.

others even more exceptional cross the Earth's orbit and at their perihelion are nearer to the Sun than to our globe. Adonis, Hermes and Apollo move nearer to the great central star than does Venus. Icarus, which was discovered in 1949 at Mount Palomar, even penetrates the orbit of Mercury.

These asteroids circulating along such peculiar orbits have given rise to certain apprehension. In 1937, Hermes came very close to the Earth (in terms of spatial distances), passing only 800,000 kilometres (500,000 miles) above its surface. Similar close approaches will certainly occur in the future. Because the orbits of the exceptional asteroids are variably inclined to the plane

The nocturnal view of a terrestrial volcanic phenomena like that illustrated here (a lava flow on Mt Etna photographed during the eruption of 1964) is probably similar to the gigantic eruptions that occur on Jupiter which is hidden under clouds.

of the ecliptic, their encounters with the Earth are arranged like secondary roads with motorways, where proper flyovers, distributing the traffic on different planes, eliminate any danger of accidents.

The origin of the minor planets has posed a difficult problem for astronomers: why is there no planet similar to the others in the Solar System circulating between Mars and Jupiter? One scientific hypothesis supposes that a planet existed there in the remote past and then, for unknown reasons, exploded and was reduced to debris. G. P. Kuiper proposed the existence of a certain initial number of planets (from five to ten) which then collided with one another, and were

destroyed and reduced to fragments. Kuiper's idea would simplify the problem, since it does not require an initial explosion with a completely unknown cause. Other scientists have thought that the minor planets have not changed since the creation of the planetary system and represent material which was never gathered together to form a true planet.

The Giant Jupiter

In the sky as well as on the Earth, one can encounter marked contrasts of size. One example occurs at the limit of the asteroid belt where the cosmic detritus (debris) which populates it ends at 778,000,000 kilometres

(483,500,000 miles) from the Sun. There, an extraordinary globe orbits whose mass is equivalent to that of all the other planets put together. This globe is Jupiter, the planet of giant size. Its equatorial diameter measures 142,850 kilometres (88,700 miles). Its volume corresponds to that of 1,319 spheres as big as the Earth. The structures of its clouds are much bigger than the Earth itself. During Jupiter's maximum approaches to the Earth it is still about four times farther from us than we are from the Sun. Its size is such that a modest telescope or even a good pair of binoculars allows one to appreciate the shape of the planet.

Ancient people considered Jupiter (or Jove) the father of the Gods. The heavenly body which represented him symbolised his splendour and majesty as it slowly crossed the sky. A very long way from the Sun, the biggest of the planets journeys along its orbit at thirteen kilometres (eight miles) per second and takes twelve Earth years to complete its orbit. The Jovian years are therefore very long, but this is compensated for by the lack of seasons because the axis of rotation of the planet is almost perpendicular to the plane of its orbit.

A strange Jovian peculiarity is its low density; on average it is only slightly more dense than water. This means that the planet is predominantly composed of light materials and that therefore it has no relationship with the Earth or the worlds which we have discussed so far.

Jupiter is enveloped in a vast atmosphere composed predominantly of hydrogen in which there are stratified clouds of methane and ammonia gases. Under these layers of poisonous, unbreathable gases, no form of life known to us could conceivably exist. In a similar manner to Venus, Jupiter's surface is invisible under compact clouds; it is believed that water vapour, which has not been found in the atmosphere, has all been precipitated to form a shell of ice. Direct measurements tell us that above the clouds a temperature of −140° C. (−212° F.) reigns; however, Jupiter's distance from the Sun suggests that it should be much colder and since the temperature is higher than expected this suggests that the planet's interior radiates a considerable amount of heat.

What is there then in the invisible, solid part of this gigantic body? Up to a few years ago it was thought that the planet had a small rocky nucleus enveloped in an ocean of ice thousands of kilometres thick. Today it is thought that the nucleus is composed largely of hydrogen, compressed under peculiar conditions.

Scientists recognise that Jupiter is a strange and puzzling planet. In 1955 it was discovered that the giant planet emitted radio waves and that it also has a strong magnetic field and an ionosphere with well-defined characteristics. Below the ionosphere there must be a stratosphere about ten kilometres (six miles) thick. Below that, the

The planet Jupiter observed on three successive occasions: fig. a in 1929; fig. b in 1933; fig. c in 1936. In figs. b and c the Great Red Spot can be seen; in fig. a it appears as a whitish oval.

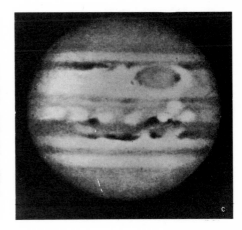

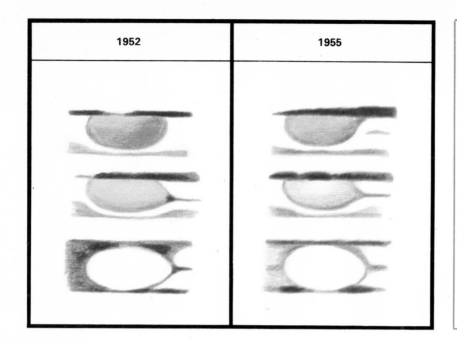

1952	1955

troposphere must be transparent and very cold at the top. About twenty kilometres (twelve miles) down in the troposphere poisonous clouds of ammonia drift which hide the planet's surface under blackness which no ray from the Sun has ever penetrated. There lies an unknown environment where extreme pressures and internal heat trigger off enormous physical phenomena. Only a reflection of what is happening on Jupiter can be seen through telescope lenses from Earth.

Jupiter displays a series of coloured bands parallel to its equator when seen through the telescope. In these bands well-defined marks can be seen which move from one hour to the next under the eye of the observer. As in the case of Mars and the Sun, the movements reveal that the planet's rotation is very rapid, with various parts rotating with different speeds. Since observers look at the surface of boundless oceans of clouds, they must logically expect this to be so. At the equator the rotation takes an average nine hours, fifty minutes and thirty seconds. In the regions corresponding to the Earth's temperate zone, the average period is a little longer —nine hours and fifty-six minutes. The solid nucleus certainly rotates with a period very close to the preceding times, but this cannot in any way be determined with certainty. As a result of its low density and the rapid rotation on its axis, Jupiter is noticeably swollen at the equator. It thus assumes a striking elliptical form.

The banded structure is produced by the rapid rotation which creates persistent cloud currents; these continually vary in detail. The bands appear in bright colours ranging from brown to carmine red, sometimes contrasting with greenish, bluish or even bright blue tints. The process which gives rise to the formation of these colours is still not perfectly understood.

In all this gigantic, continually changing meteorology, there appears in the southern hemisphere a detail which is striking because of its persistence: it is the famous Giant Red Spot, a spot with an elliptical shape, 50,000 kilometres (31,000 miles) long and 11,000 kilometres (9,320 miles) wide. The Earth's diameter is about a thousand miles greater than the smallest dimension of this Jovian feature. The Giant Red Spot was discovered in 1665 by the Italian Giovanni Domenico Cassini (1625–1712; director of the Paris Observatory) and then it was forgotten. It was rediscovered in 1878 and has been followed with interest since. From one year to the next it changes colour passing from the palest white through orange to pink to bright red. Despite these colour changes, it is the only stable form on the enormous world of Jupiter where everything is continually changing.

Irregularly but repeatedly the regions

surrounding the Giant Red Spot change enormously in form and this is well known in detail. The phenomenon takes the name of the 'South Tropical Disturbance'. It is thought that this phenomenon is the result of eruptive centres on the planet's surface which create forms in the upper atmosphere that tend to become stable because of the low temperatures. Our minds can probe beyond what is displayed in the telescope and imagine, in the heavy darkness under the clouds of ammonia which seal everything, eruptions of unbelievable intensity. Active volcanoes on Earth suggest, to a certain degree, the explosions which occur on Jupiter.

Jupiter's Moons

The skies over Jupiter are as fascinating as the planet's surface and atmosphere. Twelve moons shine there. Eight are very small, but four are truly conspicuous. In fact, two of these exceed the mass of our Moon and the largest one is bigger than the planet Mercury. In spite of the enormous distance, large telescopes enable us to observe the marks on these four moons which are worlds in their own right: worlds, however, which are extraordinarily inhospitable, without atmospheres and covered mainly in frozen gases. Since the orbits of these moons are almost edgewise to the Earth, the moons appear to oscillate from one night to the next

with respect to the planet. During their orbits when they pass in front of Jupiter, they project small but very clear circular shadows which run slowly across the planet.

When Galileo pointed his newly-invented telescope towards Jupiter on the nights of the 8th to the 11th of January, 1610, the great satellites were revealed and appeared as bright points on either side of Jupiter. From one evening to the next he saw them move; before his eyes a miniature planetary system appeared. This discovery was decisive for the defence which Galileo made of the Copernican system.

The first four satellites, called Galilean satellites (after their discoverer), were numbered in order of their distance from Jupiter: I, II, III, IV. The remaining ones have been numbered in order of their discovery from V on to XII.

Satellites I to IV of Jupiter are as big or even bigger than the Earth's satellite, the Moon. When these Jovian moons pass in front of the planet, they can be clearly seen, either as small points of light or as rather dark discs. In large telescopes, they appear to be patchy, but scientists have been unable to discover anything concrete about the nature of their surfaces. Another unanswered question is whether or not any of Jupiter's satellites possess atmospheres. Current research indicates that they do not, but it might be possible for Ganymede to have a very thin covering.

101

FROM SATURN TO REMOTE PLUTO

Saturn

So far, numerous interesting spectacles in the sky have been discussed: the lunar surface, crimson solar prominences, the crescent of Venus, and the changing colours of Mars and Jupiter. But in the most remote and cold spaces of the Solar System, something even more unusual exists. This is Saturn, the distant planet encircled with silvery rings. In a big telescope the view of its aureoles, suspended in space around a globe diffused with delicate tints, is truly fascinating. But its spectacular appearance hides a cold and inhospitable world enveloped in ice and bound like Jupiter in poisonous clouds of ammonia and methane gases.

Long ago Saturn represented the God of time. The planet's extremely slow passage across the background of stars was even calmer than that of Jupiter, and was associated with the unceasing flow of events on the Earth. A year on Saturn lasts for twenty-nine years and one hundred and sixty-six days on our world and this is the explanation of its presence for long periods in the same region of the sky.

Such a long orbital period around the Sun is linked to a very extended orbit; the radius of the orbit is 1,427 million kilometres (886,697,000 miles). Saturn is almost twice as distant from the Sun as Jupiter and almost ten times as far away from the Sun as the Earth. Because it is so remote, Saturn always appears very small in the telescope even under large magnifications.

However, in that faint image a giant world with proportions close to those of Jupiter is hidden. The equatorial diameter of the planet is 119,350 kilometres (74,161 miles); the average diameter is about 115,000 kilometres (71,458 miles) because the polar flattening is very pronounced.

To form a globe like that of Saturn, 744 spheres as big as the Earth would be needed. Because the planet is composed of very light materials, its mass is only ninety-five times greater than that of the Earth. And, as a result, the average density of Saturn is equivalent to a little more than seven-tenths of that of water. From this fact a disconcerting deduction can be made: the enormous globe and its rings would float if placed in a hypothetical ocean big enough to contain it.

Below: *Saturn, the marvel of the Solar System, as seen through a great telescope.*

Opposite page: *Diagrams showing the Solar System in perspective.*

Jupiter

Jupiter

Jupiter

This extraordinary world, although a little smaller and a little less dense than Jupiter, is practically the large planet's brother. Saturn's structure is fundamentally the same: its atmosphere is composed of hydrogen, its surface is invisible under clouds of ammonia and methane gases arranged in bands parallel to its equator. Like Jupiter, the internal heat of Saturn generates movements in its ocean of freezing clouds, which are transitory and destined to disappear eventually. The period of rotation has been obtained from studying these clouds: scientists think it is very rapid, lasting about ten hours and seventeen minutes. This is an approximate figure, naturally, for the planet's surface is invisible to us even when a very powerful telescope is used.

The atmospheric activity is much less on Saturn than on Jupiter because of its greater distance from the warming effect of the Sun. Direct measurement of the temperature gives very low values. The atmospheric regions are the only parts scientists can study and the temperature there is about 155° C. below zero (—293° F.). According to recent research, the clouds in Saturn's troposphere are stratified at much lower levels than those on Jupiter because of the colder temperature. Above the clouds there is a layer of hydrogen many tens of kilometres thick which gives the planet its particular pearly colour.

Saturn's Rings

Under the poisonous gases, the world of Saturn is hidden in permanent darkness. In contrast, the triple rings shine in the planet's skies. These rings are a unique structure in the Solar System. In spite of their solid appearance, they are only an immense swarm of particles of variable dimensions— some as fine as dust—which orbit the globe and are arranged on its equatorial plane like many independent satellites. Each element of the ring has its own orbit and follows Kepler's laws. Therefore, the particles do not move as one unified disc, but with differing speeds, that is at faster speeds closer to the centre and slower near the margin. The average rotation of the rings occurs in ten hours and thirty-two minutes.

The rings' strong reflective powers (they reflect eighty per cent of the Sun's light), have enabled us to establish that the particles are largely composed of ice. This leads to a surprising reflection: if Saturn were brought nearer to the centre of the Solar System its luminous rings would be evaporated by the Sun's heat.

Since Saturn's axis of rotation is inclined to the plane of its orbit at 26° 44′ (the inclination is a little greater than that of the Earth's axis) the rings coincide with the equatorial plane, and they undergo a seasonal event being illuminated alternately from each side by the Sun during the long Saturnian year. The inclination of the axis gives rise to another result: from the Earth we see the rings from varying points of view. They are sometimes shown fully extended, but a point is reached when we can see them in exact profile as a very thin line. Under certain conditions not even a line is visible: Saturn then appears without its rings.

The ring system is extraordinarily thin; it has been calculated to be sixteen kilometres (a little under ten miles) wide, but it is probably even thinner. The width of the rings including the gaps between is approximately 66,000 kilometres (41,000 miles). Various planets as big as the Earth could comfortably roll along side by side within it. The swarm of particles in the rings are grouped into three principal currents of different densities. There are, however, secondary currents which create finer divisions that are visible in the largest telescopes. Under favourable viewing conditions and with large telescopes, these currents appear as a multiplicity of orbits of the bodies which comprise the swarm.

Ten satellites are associated with the rings. The last satellite was discovered as recently as the 2nd of January 1967 by A. Dollfus at the Meudon Observatory in Paris. The largest of these moons, Titan, has the exact dimensions of Mercury, and it is the only one of the planetary satellites in the Solar System which possesses an atmosphere, although the gases which form it are unbreathable and consist almost entirely of methane and ammonia. The other smaller moons are bleak rocky globes or spheres of ice. The silent movement of their phases in Saturn's skies completes the splendid spectacle of the rings.

Uranus and Neptune

With the increase in the power of the telescope and with the more accurate knowledge of the movements of the celestial bodies new worlds were revealed. In 1781 in England, Sir William Herschel discovered Uranus. In 1846, Urbain Jean Joseph Leverrier (1811–77), in France and John Couch Adams (1819–92), in England, deduced the position of another planet from the disturbances of the motion of Uranus. This new planet was then found by the Berlin Observatory and

Left: *A reflecting telescope constructed by Sir Isaac Newton.*

Bottom left: *One of Sir William J. Herschel's telescopes, of his own construction. This example is two metres (6½ feet) long.*

Bottom right: *The telescope at Asiago Observatory in Padua, Italy. The mirror has a diameter of just over 1 metre (about 4 feet).*

Opposite page: *Three photographs of Saturn which show how the view of the rings seen from the Earth changes from one year to the next. In the bottom photograph the planet seems to lack rings altogether.*

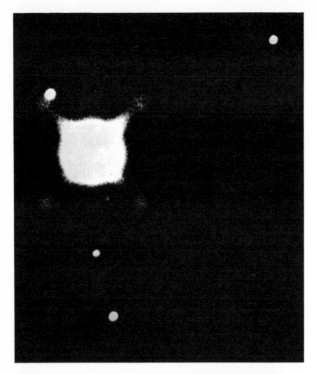

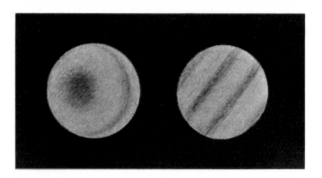

called Neptune. In 1930 a last very remote planet, named Pluto, was discovered by Clyde Tombaugh during an examination of photographic plates at Flagstaff Observatory, Arizona, U.S.A.

Even today, scientists do not know for certain whether or not they have discovered the limit of the Sun's empire.

Uranus and Neptune are two icy giants, similar to Jupiter and Saturn in structure, density and atmospheric composition. The principal difference lies in the fact that Uranus and Neptune are smaller in size, although they are still enormous when compared with the Earth. Like their larger brothers, their surfaces are permanently hidden under enormous thicknesses of poisonous clouds, overlaid by an extensive atmosphere of hydrogen. Like Jupiter and Saturn, temperature measurements tell us that under the ice which covers Uranus and Neptune internal heat is hidden. The enormous distances, however, impede our view of any traces of movement produced on their surfaces.

The first of these worlds to be discovered, Uranus, orbits at a distance of 2,870 million kilometres (1,783 million miles) from the Sun and takes eighty-four Earth years and four days to complete its orbit. The second, Neptune, circles at a distance of 4,497 million kilometres (2,794 million miles) from the centre of the Solar System and takes one hundred and sixty-four years and two hundred and eighty-nine days to complete its orbit. Both planets appear green in the telescope. The reason for this lies in the atmospheric temperature of 180° C. below zero for Uranus and about 200° C. below zero for Neptune. As a result of the intense cold, the ammonia from the colours we see, appears to be almost completely frozen. A lot of methane, however, still remains diluted in a very great thickness of hydrogen and this gives those distant planets their dark green colour.

Uranus has a diameter of 47,150 kilometres (29,300 miles). Its rotational period is ten hours and forty-nine minutes. Its rotational axis is nearly parallel to the plane of its orbit. As a result, incredible seasons alternate there because at the solstices the Sun is vertically over its poles. In the sky of Uranus, which is nineteen times as far from the Sun as the Earth, there are five moons. The biggest, Titania, has a diameter of 1,000 kilometres (621 miles).

Neptune has a diameter of 44,700 kilometres (27,770 miles) and a rotational period of fifteen hours and forty-eight minutes. While Uranus shows thin bands parallel to its equator similar to those of Jupiter and Saturn, Neptune displays only irregular marks which first appeared in observations made in 1948 at Pic du Midi in France. It is evident that extremely low temperatures have frozen all meteorological activity in the atmosphere of Neptune. Two moons circle around the desolate planet, of which the largest, Triton, is a little larger than our Moon. The smaller one is named Nereid. It is only about 200 miles in diameter and revolves in a very eccentric orbit.

Pluto

Pluto, at the remote confines of the Sun's planetary system, is a world completely different from the giant planets with atmospheres of methane and hydrogen. Pluto is slightly larger than Mercury with a diameter of about 6,000 kilometres (3,728 miles) and has a density more than ten times that of the Earth. Pluto is a rocky globe like the planets

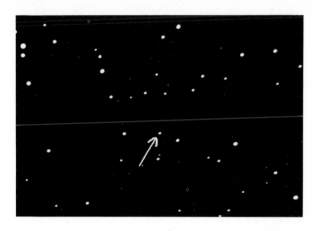

Because it is very small, only slightly larger than Mercury, Pluto is always seen as a luminous point even in the largest telescopes. The photograph shows the planet, indicated by an arrow, against a background of stars.

nearest to the Sun. Many scientists believe Pluto may be one of Neptune's ancient moons which deviated in its orbit as a satellite as a result of disturbances which intervened in the Neptunian system. This would explain its oddly-shaped orbit which is very flattened and which is unique among the planets. Pluto's orbit has a perihelion within Neptune's orbit and an aphelion in remote space.

On this distant world the temperature is between —220 to 230° C. (—428 to 446° F.). Day and night alternate with a slow rhythm of six days and nine hours, but the long days are only twilight. In the sky of the planet which probably has an atmosphere which is completely frozen, the Sun is only a bright point set in the starry vault; it shines on Pluto 2,000 times less brightly than it does on Earth.

Because of Pluto's relatively small size, it belongs to the group of so-called terrestrial planets—Mercury, Venus, the Earth and Mars—rather than to the group of large gaseous planets which include Jupiter.

Since Pluto is so remote, astronomers do not know a great deal about the planet. It is possible that Pluto is not the last planet in the Solar System, but the first of another group which is yet to be discovered. The sky may hold many more exciting secrets.

COMETS AND SHOOTING STARS

At irregular intervals the mysterious comets appear in the sky. They are of variable shape and their translucent tails extend across the sky like tenuous luminous clouds. From one night to the next, their positions slowly change against the background of the constellations. Sometimes for weeks, at other times for months, these exceptional bodies attract our attention. Then they decrease in brightness, their appearance gradually becomes faint and finally every trace disappears. However, many comets return periodically to our skies, behaving in a certain sense like planets. With a few exceptions these bodies are observable only with a telescope.

Long ago man was convinced that any happening in the sky influenced the things that happened on Earth. Comets, unexplainable and so different from the other stars, were thought to have bad influences on Earth. They were associated with wars, famine, pestilence and also natural disasters. Ancient chronicles are full of references to comets in this sense; and the popular imagination gave fantastic interpretations to their nebulous appearance. People claimed to see lances, swords, shapes of fists and serpents, and other images. The appearance of a comet was interpreted as a 'sign from heaven' and the period when it was visible was a time of anxiety and terror. Even today many people fear the consequences of a comet hitting the Earth. Scientific knowledge should completely eliminate any fears, for modern research reveals the comets, not as signs of misfortune or catastrophe, but as marvels of creation.

Although the origin and the exact nature of these spectacular heavenly bodies is in some doubt, we do know that comets obey the same laws as the other bodies in the Solar System.

Cometary Orbits

Smaller comets have a regular periodicity. They describe orbits around the Sun very similar to those of the planets but much more elongated or elliptical in form. Therefore, at the perihelion they pass very close to the Sun, while at the aphelion they pass through the remotest and coldest regions of the Solar System. This periodicity was discovered by the Englishman Edmund Halley in 1705 while he was studying the various appearances recorded in the chronicles of a comet which now bears his name. Halley noted that the three comets which appeared in 1531, 1607 and 1682 had more or less described the same orbit. He deduced that he was dealing with the same body and predicted its return in 1758. Halley died in 1742 and could not check his prediction. In December 1758 his comet reappeared punctually and reached the perihelion in 1759. This comet intersects the Earth's orbit when it is closest to the Sun, while at its aphelion it almost touches the orbit of very remote Pluto. Continuing to circulate with its period of seventy-six years (which might be called the comet's year), Halley's Comet returned to blaze in the Earth's skies in 1910. Its next return is anticipated in 1986. Halley's Comet is an exception because it is a visible comet with a relatively brief period.

The comet Mrkos, which was clearly seen on the warm August nights of 1957, had never been observed before. Astronomers have found that it also has a periodicity, but so long that several thousand years will pass before it is seen again. The beautiful Donati comet of 1858 will return only in the distant year 4000. Other sister comets will never be seen again. The magnificent comet Arend-Roland, which traced its silvery tail across the violet skies of evening at the end of April 1957, seems to be lost in space. Probably the comets compose a sort of cloud which circles around the Sun at an extraordinarily great distance beyond Pluto. From their distant recesses, attraction by gravitational forces can pull them as far as the Earth's orbit. Some, deviated from their orbits by the attraction of the big planets, are stabilised

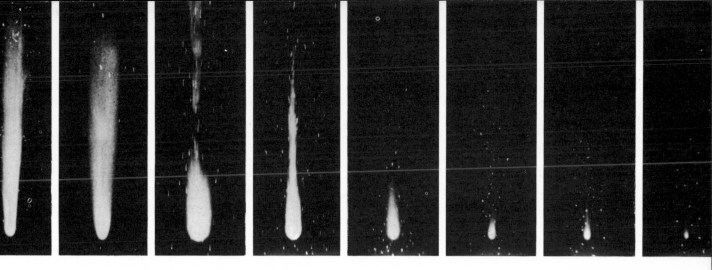

Above: *Edmund Halley's great comet photographed on successive nights at Mount Wilson Observatory.*

Below: *The painting illustrates the ancient beliefs that the mysterious heavenly bodies with tails (the comets) had an unfavourable influence and that their appearance foreshadowed wars, destruction, plagues, etc.*

within the Solar System and become short period types. Others remain on extremely elongated ellipses and return to perihelion at intervals of thousands of years.

The Appearance of Comets

When comets first emerge from the depths of space, they appear in big telescopes as small indistinct, rounded bodies. Slowly, as their distance from the Sun is reduced, they become nebulous and start to develop a bright streak, the 'tail' which is always directed away from the Sun; meanwhile, they increase in brightness. At perihelion the tail reaches its maximum length, while the head of the comet develops spectacular phenomena which produce rapid changes in its appearance. The tail of the comet of 1811 was 176,000,000 kilometres (110,000,000 miles) long; that of 1843, the longest so far recorded, even reached 320,000,000 kilometres (200,000,000 miles). It is solar energy which activates a comet and which makes it produce the long tail which gives it such an imposing appearance. After perihelion, the tail is inverted in its position. When a comet approaches the Sun the tail follows it; as it moves away from the Sun the tail precedes it. While the body moves towards cold remote space, its tail becomes more tenuous and disappears as the comet regains its original pale nebulous aspect. After a certain time, generally some months, not even the most powerful telescopes can distinguish it.

When a comet is close to the Earth, observers can see that its head is composed of a diffuse mass, the 'coma', which contains a small, brilliant luminous centre, the 'nucleus'. The nucleus is the heart of the comet, and is of extraordinarily small size. While the diffuse head can attain dimensions similar to those of Jupiter and Saturn, or even bigger, the brilliant nucleus according to recent research has a diameter which does not exceed some hundreds of metres. A comet's mass is insignificant and does not provoke any disturbance in the motions of the planets it approaches.

The Structure of Comets

A comet's nucleus is composed of gas, meteoric material and dust. Far from the Sun, the gas is frozen. However, when the comet nears the blazing Sun the gas starts to evaporate and surrounds the nucleus with the coma. Then the solar wind strikes the evaporating gas and it is blown out in the form of a tail. The wind which emanates from the Sun is a complex of particles, atoms and electrons, projected continuously into space. Just as the terrestrial winds extend long wisps of smoke from chimneys, the solar wind extends the comet's gas and finest dust into space. Thus the phenomenon of the tail being always aligned away from the Sun is explained.

A comet's tail shines partly as a result of the luminosity of the gas struck by the ultraviolet rays emitted by the Sun, and in part because the impalpable dust reflects the sunlight directly. The stars, seen through the tail, shine undimmed or are just slightly concealed.

What is the density of these apparently delicate bodies in space? It has been calculated that 500 cubic kilometres (310 cubic miles) of a comet's tail contains, at the most, the amount of material which is found in a cubic centimetre of air. Obviously, therefore, comets are composed of rather light material. Between the 18th and 19th of May 1910 the Earth passed through the tail of Halley's Comet. Some people feared the end of the world that night, but in reality no one on the Earth was aware of anything. And yet the comets, made almost of nothing, are clearly visible phenomena.

The material which the solar wind blows away from the comet is lost in space and is never recovered. A few journeys to perihelion are sufficient for small comets to lose their envelope of gas and be reduced to little more than a group of meteors. This is why the most spectacular comets are the 'new' comets, those that have periods of thousands of years and that have never been observed before (or perhaps have no periodicity and appear only once in the neighbourhood of the Sun). Comets are so tenuous that the gravitational force of the Sun or even a big planet like Jupiter can produce tidal phenomena capable of dividing the nucleus into two or more parts; this accelerates their destruction. On the 21st of October 1965 the

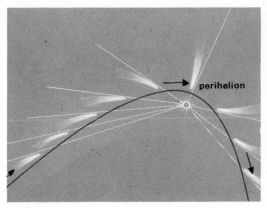
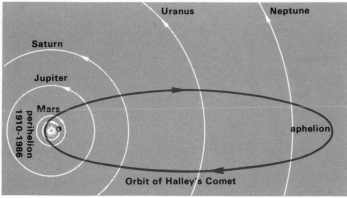

Above left: *A diagram illustrating the orientation of a comet's tail, which is always away from the Sun.*

Above right: *The orbit of Halley's Comet.*

Below: *Two photographs of the head of a big comet showing the initial part of its tail.*

Bottom right: *The head of a comet of medium size compared with the Earth (lower right-hand corner).*

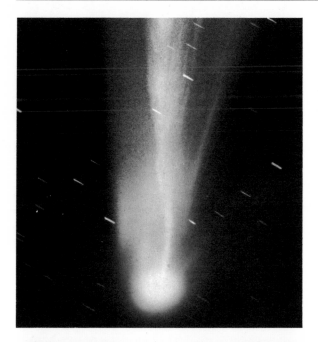

beautiful comet Ikeya-Seki (which had been discovered on the 18th of September 1965 by two amateur Japanese astronomers) passed only 465,000 kilometres (288,938 miles) from the blazing photosphere of the Sun. Two weeks later observers saw that the nucleus was broken into three parts which were drawing away from one another. Phenomena of this sort can be accentuated until the comet is reduced to a swarm of meteors and dust dispersed along its orbit. The body is thus destroyed and only fragments remain in space.

During the Earth's journey around the Sun, our globe passes through the dust of dead comets and our skies are lit with the fleeting sparkles of shooting stars. When minute debris from comets penetrates the

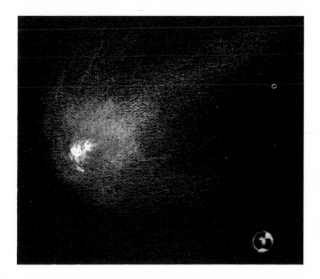

111

Earth's upper atmosphere, it is heated up until it evaporates or dissolves. In its very rapid flight the debris shines vividly and gives the impression of a star falling suddenly from the vault of the sky. Even very small meteors weighing less than a gramme can appear as intensely luminous objects. The large meteors can resist the phenomena of heating and evaporation for a long time: they have vividly coloured and diffuse tracks sometimes with explosive phenomena, which are called fireballs (bolides). Fragments or entire fireballs can reach the Earth's surface. Thus parts of celestial bodies originating in the deepest and most remote parts of space, which have journeyed for millions of years, arrive on Earth where their structure and age can be investigated.

Shooting Stars

The link between shooting stars and comets was demonstrated by the Italian astronomer Schiaparelli in 1866 after the German physicist Ernst F. F. Chladni (1756–1827) had first suggested it in 1794. Astronomers in Schiaparelli's time were able to witness at first hand the death of a comet. The periodic comet Biela was a regular visitor to the Earth's skies for sixty years before 1846. In that year it appeared divided into two smaller comets, each with its own tail. These were seen again, more widely separated and fainter, in 1852. Subsequent periodic returns in 1859 and 1866 were awaited in vain, but on the 27th of November 1872 the Earth passed through the orbit of the vanished Biela and the sky that night was inundated in a marvellous shower of shooting stars.

The Earth encounters several such swarms during the year. The best known are those of 'Saint Lorenzo's tears' seen between the 10th and the 12th of August and which seem to emanate from the constellation of Perseus (which gives the name of Perseids to the meteors which compose the swarm). These are the remains of the comet *1862 III*. Sometimes the Earth passes exactly through the point in a cometary orbit where the ancient nucleus was found. Then an exceptional shower of shooting stars occurs and the entire sky seems to fall apart in coloured tracks of

Above: *The splendid comet Ikeya-Seki photographed from Japan on the 29th of October 1956, eight days after the disruption of its nucleus which was produced by the gravitational attraction of the Sun.*

Below: *The comet, Biela, as it appeared in the sky in 1846, divided into two smaller comets.*

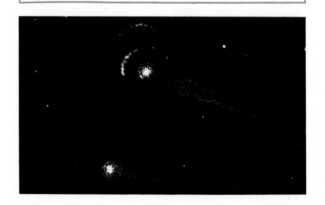

light, which continue for hours without interruption. During these great showers there is scarcely any danger; the bulk of the meteors are destroyed in the atmosphere and only in very rare cases do they reach the Earth's surface.

Some of these cases, however, have left imposing craters on the Earth similar to those on the Moon. The most famous is Meteor Crater in Arizona, which is 180 metres (approx. 600 feet) deep and 1,250 metres (approx. three quarters of a mile) across. Fragments of meteoric iron have been found around the edges indicating an explosion which shattered the meteorite on the moment of impact. It has been calculated that the fireball weighed many millions of tons when it fell. The arrival of this enormous mass took place many thousands of years ago

and we can study only the effects it had on the land surface. The actual fragments of the meteorite (probably iron and nickel) are now buried about four hundred feet below the surface, most likely to one side of the floor of the immense crater.

More precise information is known about the meteorite of Wanovara, which fell in Siberia on 30th June 1908, fortunately in an uninhabited area covered with forests. For hundreds of kilometres the sky seemed to burst into flames; tens of square kilometres of dense forests were razed to the ground and whole herds of reindeer were destroyed in an instant. It is believed that this fireball weighed not less than 40,000 tons. When this fireball passed through the sky, it was followed by loud thunderclaps which were heard as far away as six hundred miles. Up to one or two hundred miles away, people and even horses were blown off their feet. Waves of earthquake shocks were recorded which travelled round the Earth several times, rivers rose and houses and buildings collapsed. At a distance of two hundred and fifty miles from the area where the meteorite fell, witnesses described flames which spurted into the sky that may have reached a height of twelve miles from the Earth's surface. Despite all of this, events of this sort are too exceptional to rouse worry. Meteors must be regarded not with apprehension but with interest as they bring information from space.

The minerals of these meteors are the same as those we find on Earth. They have been studied and structures have been traced which indicate the processes of fused materials cooling under high pressure. This fact is surprising, and is explained only by the theory that meteors must be derived from the interiors of one or more shattered and broken planets. Studies made of the radioactive elements contained in meteors to determine their age (as is done for rocks on Earth) seem to date the cosmic catastrophe which gave rise to meteorites as occurring about four thousand million years ago.

Some isolated meteors, unattached to the orbits of comets, may be genuine examples of minor planets. Probably the events developed like this: the principal residue of the very ancient planetary catastrophe was scattered in the belt between Mars and Jupiter, but a part of it was associated with gas molecules and debris which formed the Solar System, and thus formed nuclei of comets through a very slow process. This is only an hypothesis. However, it seems to help explain the otherwise mysterious shooting stars and splendid but fragile comets.

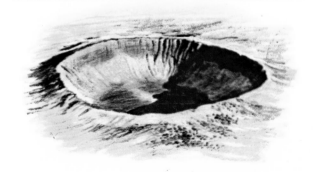

Left: *When the Earth passes through a point in space where an ancient comet's nucleus is found, an exceptional shower of shooting stars occurs.*

Below: *Meteor crater in the Arizona desert— the most famous meteoric crater on Earth.*

Part Four

THE STARRY UNIVERSE

THE CONSTELLATIONS OF THE SKY

When the lights of twilight fade in the west and the red sunset turns to an intense violet, night advances from the east and spreads stars over the sky. The Milky Way extends to the horizon as a pale silvery band.

The Milky Way presented a puzzle to man before telescopes were invented. Without the aid of any astronomical instruments, it looks like a band of mist in the sky. However, through the lens of a telescope, the Milky Way can be seen as a dense cloud of individual stars. On moonlit cloudless nights, it is sometimes possible to detect some of the stars which make up the beautiful, twinkling band in our skies.

The reason that the Milky Way forms into a band or belt in the sky is found in the shape of our stellar system, and Earth's position in it. Our galaxy of stars is shaped like a giant wheel, with Earth located fairly near the rim. When we look through the centre of the galaxy towards the distant rim, we are looking through a great thickness of stars. They, therefore, appear close together in the sky, and form what we call the Milky Way.

Prehistoric man, who drew hairy mammoths and herds of wild bison on the walls of caves, studied the sky overflowing with stars and noted that their positions did not change with time. The shape we now call the Great Bear has been found roughly scratched on shells from the Stone Age. Homer in the *Iliad,* describing the marvellous sculpture with which the god Vulcan had decorated Achilles' shield, spoke of the 'Pleiades and the Hyades, and the tempestuous star of Orion, and the Great Bear'. These constellations are as familiar today as they were long ago. Ptolemy named the forty-eight constellations discovered up to his time.

Much later, navigators who sailed into the southern hemisphere discovered and grouped the stars into constellations to which they gave the names of great discoveries of the time, such as the Microscope and the Telescope, or even animals such as the Toucan, or legendary creatures like the Phoenix. Other figures were added, meanwhile, in the northern skies by various astronomers who sought to name the many stars which remained outside Ptolemy's groupings.

Ptolemy also gave the stars in his catalogue a classification based on their apparent brightness; this classification has remained up to the present time, as have the names of the constellations. The brightest stars are of the 'first magnitude' while the faintest, only just visible to the naked eye (in the time of Ptolemy no optical instruments existed) were of the 'sixth magnitude'. Since the word 'magnitude' can create confusion, it should be pointed out immediately that it has nothing to do with the dimensions of the stars. The magnitude of stars is a convenient and necessary system of classifying their brightness, independent of the fact that distant giant stars can appear faint when compared with smaller stars, which appear very bright because they are close to us. In modern usage, the Ptolemaic scale has been extended by powerful optical instruments. The giant telescope of Mount Palomar is able to photograph stars of a magnitude of twenty-three, for example.

With its mythical figures, its legendary heroes, and its fabulous animals, outlined in groups of brilliant, twinkling lights, the 'heaven of fixed stars' where the constellations appear has always extended an irresistible invitation to men to attempt to identify its elements.

Searching for the constellations and tracing the principal stars is not difficult, provided that one proceeds, step by step, by constructing imaginary but simple lines. One should not expect to see exact images of each figure which the star groupings are

The northern starry sky depicted on a print from the first part of the eighteenth century shows figures primarily representing animals and mythical persons, after which the constellations are named.

PLANISPHÆRII COELESTIS HEMISPHÆRIUM SEPTENTRIONALE

Calculatum *ad finem Anni MDCC, pro Ævo XVIII præsente: multis Stellis auctum et editum a* CAROLO ALLARD, *Amstelo Batavo, Cum Privilegio Potentissimorum D. D. Ordinum Hollandiæ et Westfrisiæ*

Proportio Stellarum Fixarum cum Diametro Terræ

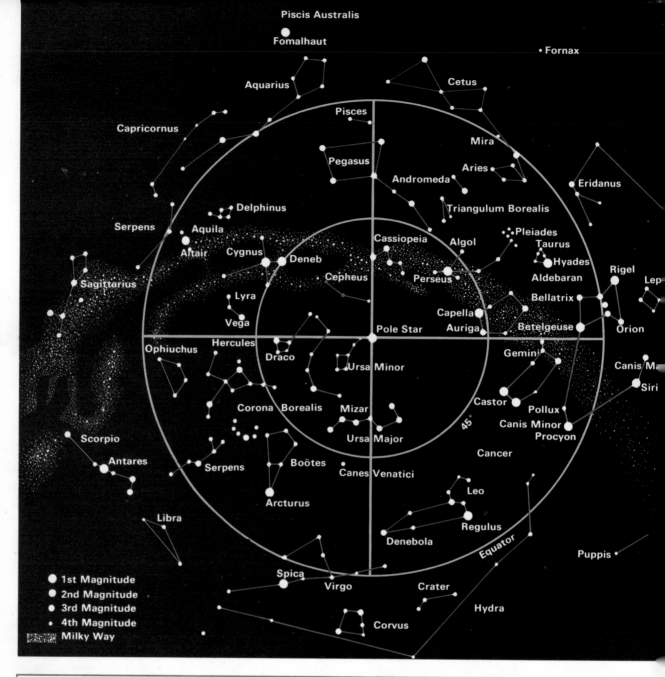

The following labels appear on the star map:

Piscis Australis
Fomalhaut
• Fornax
Aquarius
Cetus
Capricornus
Pisces
Mira
Pegasus
Aries •
• Eridanus
Andromeda
Triangulum Borealis
Delphinus
Serpens
Aquila
•• Pleiades
Altair
Cygnus
Cassiopeia
Algol
Taurus
Deneb
Hyades
Sagittarius
Cepheus
Perseus
Aldebaran
Rigel
Lyra
Capella
Bellatrix
Lep
Vega
Pole Star
Auriga
Betelgeuse
Hercules
Orion
Ophiuchus
Draco
Ursa Minor
Gemini
Canis M
Castor
Siri
Scorpio
Corona Borealis
Mizar
Pollux
Antares
Canis Minor
Serpens
Boötes
Ursa Major
Procyon
Libra
Arcturus
Canes Venatici
Cancer
Leo
Regulus
Denebola
Equator
Puppis •
Spica
Crater
● 1st Magnitude
Virgo
Hydra
● 2nd Magnitude
Corvus
● 3rd Magnitude
• 4th Magnitude
Milky Way

The Northern starry sky with the principal stars and constellations and the band of the Milky Way. As the equator divides the Earth, there is a celestial equator which divides the starry vault into two hemispheres.

supposed to represent. The guide constellation is without doubt the Great Bear. If it is taken as a starting point we can immediately find the Pole Star and then move in any direction to find other constellations.

The Great Bear, also called The Plough, The Big Dipper, or Charles's Wain, is visible at all times of the night and at all seasons. It rotates around the celestial pole (the point where the imaginary prolongation of the Earth's axis pierces the celestial vault) and is the principal constellation in the 'circumpolar' group. When winter

advances, the Great Bear can be seen at night low on the northern horizon; when spring is well advanced it is high above the same horizon. It has a characteristic shape: a large quadrilateral which recalls the four wheels of a carriage formed by four stars and an irregular alignment of another three which form the shaft. If we link, in our imagination, the two rear wheels of the wain or carriage and prolong the imaginary line to the right of the wain itself (it does not matter in which position the wain is found) we encounter an almost isolated star of

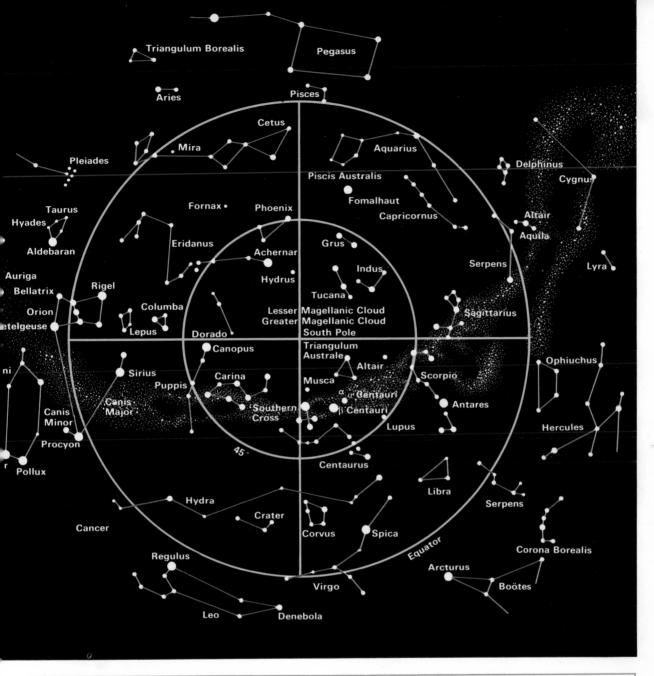

The southern starry sky is illustrated here with its constellations, its principal stars and the band of the Milky Way. This diagram and the preceding one represent the entire celestial sphere.

second magnitude; this is the Pole (or North) Star which marks the North Pole of the celestial sphere. If we observe the region around the Pole Star carefully, we can find a smaller and fainter wain at the end of the shaft of the Great Bear, disposed parallel with it but in an inverted sense. This is the Little Bear (Little Dipper or Little Wain) which includes the Pole Star.

Because of its position, above the terrestrial North Pole, the Pole Star is found at the zenith (the highest point in the sky), while the celestial equator is at the horizon. For those

who live about halfway between the terrestrial equator and the North Pole, the Pole Star shines halfway between the horizon and the zenith, and thus determines a part of sky which never sinks below the horizon but only turns every twenty-four hours as a result of the Earth's movement along its orbit. The remaining part of the sky is visible successively at various months of the year because of the circular movement of the Earth around the Sun, the point from which we see the celestial vault varying each day. It is evident that looking at the sky at

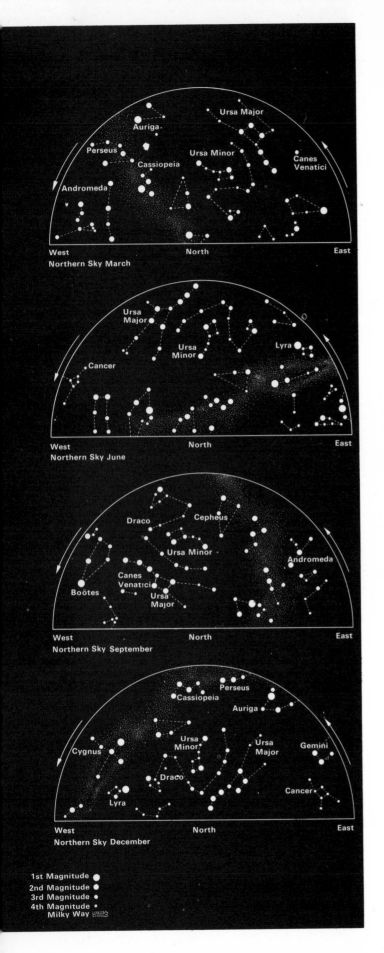

Northern Sky March
West   North   East

Northern Sky June
West   North   East

Northern Sky September
West   North   East

Northern Sky December
West   North   East

1st Magnitude
2nd Magnitude
3rd Magnitude
4th Magnitude
Milky Way

the same time every six months the constellations will appear in opposite positions in the sky.

Between the two Bears a group of rather faint stars indicate the twisted coils of the mythical dragon, Draco. However, continuing beyond the Pole Star along the line which enabled us to find it, about the same distance which separates the Pole Star from the Great Bear, we encounter a small irregularly-shaped constellation: this is Cepheus the husband of Cassiopeia, legendary queen of Ethiopia. The queen stands out on the Milky Way, not far from her husband continuing along the same line which served to find Cepheus. Cassiopeia's five rather bright principal stars form a large rather open W, clearly defined against the silvery dust of the Milky Way, which lies high above our horizons on winter nights.

From the Pole Star on a lovely summer's night an imaginary line can be traced more or less perpendicular to the line drawn through the Great Bear, the Pole Star and Cassiopeia. If we follow this line it will bring us near the zenith, and there we find Vega, the principal star of the small constellation Lyra, and the most brilliant in the northern sky. Its name is taken from Arabic like many other star names. In astronomy the constellations are distinguished by Latin names and their principal stars are indicated by letters from the Greek alphabet in decreasing order of magnitude. Therefore, Vega is also known as Alpha Lyrae (α Lyrae).

Even though it may seem surprising, in 12,000 years time splendid Vega will be the Pole Star. When discussing the Moon in the chapter on tides and eclipses mention was made of the slow displacement in direction of the terrestrial axis, called the precession, caused by the attraction of the Sun and Moon on the equatorial swelling of the Earth. It is not, therefore, Vega which is moving from its place in the heavens, but the imaginary extension of the Earth's axis of rotation which slowly moves towards the star. As a result of the precession, the imaginary extension of the terrestrial axis describes a great cone in the sky over a long period of 27,000 years. In 5,600 years the Pole Star will be Alpha of Cepheus, in 12,000

years it will be Vega, in 29,000 years it will return to Alpha of the Little Bear. Consequently constellations which pass below the horizon today will become circumpolar in the future, while those that are circumpolar today will only be visible seasonally.

In the summer sky, to the east of Vega, the Milky Way is spread across the sky and there four stars form a great cross, the constellation Cygnus which is near the zenith. To the south-east of Cygnus lie three stars in a line

121

which form the constellation Aquila. Lower down, where the Milky Way seems to break up into clouds of light, two great constellations trail across our horizon. These are Sagittarius in the east and Scorpio to the west. Scorpio symbolises the arachnid which has given it its name; its curved tail twists through the splendour of the Milky Way, while its claws extend towards the west. In Scorpio's heart a star burns which is flame coloured: this is Antares which in Greek means the 'rival of Mars'.

Sagittarius and Scorpio are a part of the Zodiac, the group of constellations against which the Sun moves in its journey during the year. The belt which includes them contains the extension in the sky of the plane of the ecliptic of the Earth's axis; a part of it is south of the celestial equator and another part is north. There are twelve constellations of the Zodiac, one for each month of the year, and they are named Aries The Ram, Taurus The Bull, Gemini The Twins, Cancer The Crab, Leo The Lion, Virgo The Virgin, Libra The Scales, Scorpius The Scorpion, Sagittarius The Archer, Capricornus The Goat, Aquarius The Water-Bearer and Pisces The Fishes. The word Zodiac in Greek signifies 'circle of animals'. These constellations have a very ancient origin which is probably to be found in Egypt (the 'Denderah stone' was discovered at the Temple of Isis in Denderah, Egypt, and it represented constellations known more than 2,000 years ago) from where they were imported to Europe. They were extremely important to ancient peoples, since they have always been very prominent in representations of the sky and for millennia have been thought to regulate the lives of men.

As summer turns to autumn and the pale Milky Way moves the splendours of Aquila (The Eagle) and Cygnus (The Swan) towards the west, a great quadrilateral of rather faint stars dominates the sky accompanied to the east by an extension of three stars which seem to form an enlarged copy of the Great Bear. The Great Bear on these nights is low on the northern horizon, while its big copy is in the southern zone of the sky just below the zenith. The great square represents Pegasus, the fabulous winged horse tamed by Neptune; the extension of three stars is Andromeda, mythical daughter of Cassiopeia. Below Pegasus, towards the south, there is the faint constellation of Pisces.

Still lower, between Pisces and Sagittarius two other zodiacal constellations occur which lack bright stars; they are Aquarius and Capricorn. To the east of Pisces, but lower in the sky, the vast zone of Cetus (The Whale) extends. It has an irregular outline composed of faint stars.

The splendid winter night sky advances with the shortening of the days. On January nights, when the frost grips the Earth and the air is as clear as crystal, the magnificence of the night sky extends above us in great constellations rich in bright and coloured stars. At the zenith, in the dust of the Milky Way, Auriga (The Charioteer) can be seen, where Capella, one of the brightest stars in the sky, shines. Between Auriga and Cassiopeia in the Milky Way, we find Perseus. A little lower, but still very high above our horizon, Taurus lies, easily recognisable because it includes the Pleiades, a small group of tiny stars disposed in a way which resembles a slightly modified Little Bear. The eye of Taurus, Aldebaran, is accompanied by tiny stars similar to the Pleiades but sparser; these are the Hyades.

Exactly to the south of Auriga, Orion the mythical hunter is prominent. It is represented by four stars which form a vertical quadrilateral at the centre of which are three stars close together in a line (the giant's belt), followed immediately to the south by three fainter stars (the sword which hangs from the belt). To the north-east of the quadrilateral is orange-coloured Betelgeuse (in Arabic 'the giant's shoulder'); to the south-west is Rigel (in Arabic 'the giant's leg') dazzling bluish-white. To the left of Orion, looking south, and a little below, shines Sirius, the most splendid of all stars.

In winter, to the west of Taurus, the small zodiacal constellation Aries moves towards the horizon. Towards the east the great quadrilateral of Gemini rises, of which the principal stars, Castor and Pollux pass almost at the zenith in late winter to early spring. Below Gemini, immediately to the east of the Milky Way, Procyon shines in Canis Minor (The Little Dog). Like a hunter, Orion is given two dogs; as well as Canis Minor he has Canis Major in whose eye the splendid Sirius is set.

Spring brings Leo lying between the zenith and the celestial equator, followed by Virgo which is exactly on the equator. The principal star in Leo is Regulus, blue-white in colour and easy to find by tracing an imaginary line south from the two stars in The Plough nearest to the shaft. In Virgo another star of the same colour as Regulus shines: this is Spica. To the south of this, groups of small stars trace long Hydra (The Sea Serpent). To the north, near the Great Bear, is the small constellation of The Hunting Dogs (Canes Venatici).

As spring advances, the constellation Boötes, the shepherd and farmer of ancient legend, rises higher in the sky. Its principal star, Arcturus, is orange and is found exactly along a line through the shaft of The Plough. Looking to the east there is a ring of stars, the Corona Borealis (The Northern Crown), then extensive constellations lacking bright stars, such as Hercules, Ophiuchus (The Serpent-Bearer) and Serpens. Low near the southern horizon the faint stars of Libra precede Scorpio, and we again find the summer Milky Way with the splendours of Cygnus and Sagittarius. So our rapid traverse of the seasonal skies is completed.

Without a doubt, the age-old delight of watching the sky will never be obsolete. In times to come when men travel freely in space, the stars will serve as their guides and signposts, just as they have in times past when men first started on their voyages of exploration.

Johann Kepler (1571-1630) was a German astronomer whose particular studies of planetary motion laid the foundations for modern astronomy. In 1600 he was appointed court mathematician in Prague where he lived and worked for 28 years. The illustration shows Johann Kepler's Belvedere Observatory in Prague, Czechoslovakia, with an instrument of his time which was used to determine the positions of the stars; in this way the geometry of the heavens was studied. Only the introduction of the telescope has enabled astronomers to study the physics of the heavenly bodies.

THE REALM OF THE STARS

The realm of the stars extends far beyond our Solar System. The glittering night-sky is exceptionally beautiful, but until recent years it has proved almost impossible to study. However, with improvement in astronomical instruments, stellar astronomy has developed very rapidly and is now one of the biggest areas of research.

The Distance of Stars

For thousands of years man has asked, 'How far away are the stars?' If we look at any constellation on a certain night and then look at it again six months later, we cannot see the slightest change. Nevertheless, the Earth travels half its orbit in six months and thus it moves about 300,000,000 kilometres (186,500,000 miles). This enormous distance does not produce even the smallest deformity of the perspective from which we see the stars. Therefore, these bodies are disposed at an extraordinarily great distance.

Since the first part of the nineteenth century, extremely precise astronomical measurements have revealed that some stars show a very slight movement in relation to others, and this occurs every six months. These determinations have enabled scientists to measure the distances to the stars by means of a system of triangulation, similar to that used to determine distances within the Solar System and on the Earth. The first successful attempt was made by the Englishman Thomas Henderson (1798–1844) in 1832, and the German astronomer F. W. Bessel obtained the first precise measurement in December 1838. From then on, the measurements increased in number. In 1916 Walter Adams at the Mount Wilson Observatory, California, introduced a new method based on data obtained using the spectroscope. From that time on, astronomers were able to probe the sky in detail.

The closest of all the stars shines in the southern sky in the constellation Centaurus, which is situated to the south of Hydra. This is the star Proxima Centauri, the nearest star

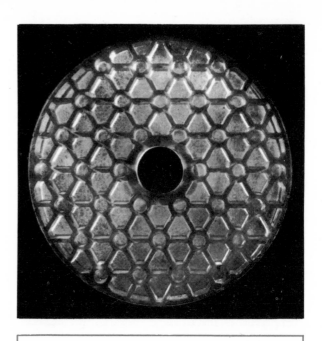

Above: *The objective of the Hale telescope at Mount Palomar in California is a concave mirror five metres (200 inches) in diameter.*
Right: *The tube of an astronomical telescope with its supports.*

of Centaurus (The Centaur) despite the fact that light from the star takes four and two-tenths years to reach Earth. Our minds cannot imagine the immense abyss which lies between us and the stars, but let us take an astronautical example to provide some idea of the distance. If we have at our disposal a space ship capable of completing a flight around the Earth's equator in one hour which is launched towards Proxima Centauri, it would take 120,000 years to arrive there.

However, Proxima Centauri is the closest star, and splendid Sirius, another close star, shines on us across an abyss more than twice as great—eight and seven-tenths light-years away. Altair, in the heart of the constellation Aquila, is four times farther—sixteen and four-tenths light-years from us. From brilliant Vega the light takes twenty-six and four tenths light-years to reach us and if our great majestic Sun took the place of Vega, we would see it only as a faint, insignificant star.

If a star is low on the horizon its light must travel through a greater thickness of atmosphere and, therefore, it twinkles more than if it is directly overhead.

Now we can understand that only the light-year, a unit of measurement giving the distance travelled by light in a year (one light-year is equal to 9,468,000,000,000 kilometres or 5,880,000,000,000 miles), can adequately represent the enormous space between Earth and the stars.

Beyond Earth's immediate neighbours, in the constellation Orion, red Betelgeuse is 586 light-years from us and bluish Rigel 880 light-years.

Like our Sun, the faint lights of night are really globes of high temperature gas radiating enormous quantities of energy. But no telescope can reveal them as discs. Because of their great distance from us they are only luminous points even in the biggest instruments. Only a thin ray of light which the moving layers of the Earth's atmosphere break and agitate reaches us from them. It is the Earth's moving atmosphere which makes stars appear to twinkle; in space such stars shine steadily. The thin luminous rays of light which do reach Earth, however, contain an enormous quantity of information, which astronomers patiently collect and eventually catalogue and study, so that nothing is lost.

The Brightness and Colour of Stars

On the star chart on page 118 there is a key in the lower left-hand corner which indicates the magnitude or brightness of stars.

The Greek Hipparchus invented the system of classification of the stars according to their brightness. The brightest stars which could be seen with the naked eye belonged to the first magnitude and the faintest stars belonged to the sixth magnitude. This system is still followed today. Of course, the series of magnitude is now continued for faint stars which can only be seen with a telescope—stars of magnitude 7 and so on. The same magnitude scale is also used to express the brightness of planets which can be seen as sparkling lights.

When one looks at the night sky, the difference in colours of the stars can be readily seen. Some stars appear to have a bluish tint, some are white or yellow, others are orange or red.

The difference in colour of stars depends on their relative temperatures, as we shall see in discussing 'white dwarfs', 'red giants' and others.

The Analysis of Stars

We know that Fraunhofer's black lines which divide the solar spectrum enable us to make chemical analyses of the Sun. It is also possible to make the same analyses of the stellar spectra, even if they are weak in comparison as a result of the faint light, since the elements which we find in the Sun and on Earth appear in the most remote stars. We can determine the chemistry of the stars as well as measure their superficial temperatures. Their spectral characteristics and their colours enable us to do this.

As incandescent metal is brightest when it is hottest—passing from dark red to light red and white—so the temperatures of the stars vary, ranging from types with red light to those with white or bluish light. The black lines in their spectra give us further information about what is happening in their atmospheres, about their rotation and their movements nearer to or farther away from us. Also the measurement of their positions enables us to determine their masses. This is possible with the pairs of stars which are bound by mutual attraction: using the laws

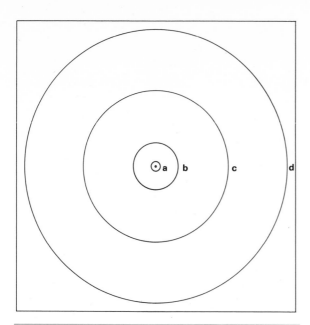

Diameters of stars compared with that of the Sun: the Pole Star, fig. a, *has a diameter eleven times greater;* Aldebaran, *fig.* b, *fifty times;* Beta of Pegasus, *fig.* c, *one hundred and five times; and* Betelgeuse, *fig.* d, *two hundred and eighty times.*

of gravitation we can calculate their masses. The information acquired in this way is then applied to other stars, based on well-defined correlations.

This extraordinary deciphering of the faint messages which reach us from infinite space is the result of work by pioneers in astronomy: Father Angelo Secchi of the Vatican Observatory, who in 1862 applied the spectroscope to the starry universe; the Dane E. Hertzprung and the American H. N. Russell, who in 1911 and 1913 found a fundamental relationship between the luminosity and the temperature of the stars; and Sir A. S. Eddington, who in 1924 discovered the basic relation which ties a star's mass to its luminosity. As a result of their work, the secrets of the most remote universe have been revealed and will be studied further and explored in the future.

The Exceptional Stars

The splendid star Sirius is about twice as heavy as our Sun, about twice as large and very much hotter. Its light is forty times stronger than that of the Sun. In spite of this, it is so bright only because it is relatively close. In the giant Orion, which is above Sirius in the sky, there are even more marvellous stars, although they appear fainter because they are farther away. The central star in the belt of Orion is blue in colour, at least 600 times brighter than the Sun, ten times bigger and four times hotter at the surface; it is thought that its mass is more than twenty times that of the Sun. Rigel, the star at the giant's feet, is still more imposing. It is classified astronomically as a 'blue super giant'. It blazes like twenty thousand suns and its mass is at least forty times that of the Sun. If it were substituted for our Sun, in an instant its blazing heat would destroy every trace of life on Earth.

Betelgeuse, the alpha star in Orion, is a 'red super giant'—a very rare type of star. Its dimensions are equal to about three hundred times those of the Sun. If the Sun were placed at Betelgeuse's centre, the Earth would orbit within the star's interior. Its temperature is relatively low (about 3,000° C.) and its density is less than one-millionth of that of the Sun. Therefore, it is less dense than the air we breath. Probably, in its centre, a white or bluish star is hidden by a chromosphere tens of millions of kilometres thick. Its spectrum suggests the continual presence of gigantic prominences which erupt continually over all its surface.

An even more exceptional example in this category of extraordinary stars is given by one of the components in the system of Epsilon in Auriga composed of two stars linked by mutual gravitation. The larger of the two has such a low temperature (1,700° C.) that it radiates more infra-red rays than light rays. Its mass equals 25 times that of the Sun, but its diameter is 2,000 times that of the Sun. Its interior could contain the entire planetary system—from Mercury to Saturn —known to ancient people. In this red globe matter is so tenuous that it exceeds imagination: compared with it Betelgeuse is a relatively compact body.

'White dwarfs' are another unusual type of star, of which the most important example is represented by a faint star which accompanies Sirius. This is the 'Companion of Sirius' or 'Sirius B', which Americans call 'The Baby'. Sirius B is not very different from the Sun in mass and in superficial

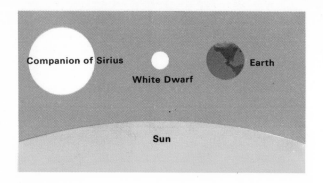

Companion of Sirius

White Dwarf

Earth

Sun

temperature; however, its volume is 100,000 times smaller. So much material contained in such a small star carries truly extraordinary consequences. On the surface of Sirius B the gravity is 250,000 times stronger than on Earth; a teaspoonful of its material would weigh more than a ton. Other white dwarfs are still smaller, like Van Maanen's Star which has a diameter smaller than that of the Earth. However, one of the group is about as big as Mercury. These very heavy microstars exist because their matter is in a particular state which the great Italian physicist Enrico Fermi (1901–54) called 'degenerate': that is, within their interiors the nuclei of the atoms are in contact. This is a situation which does not occur on Earth, or in the normal stars.

The giants, the super giants and the white dwarfs are the exception, not the rule. Innumerable groups of stars similar or even much fainter than our Sun populate space, even if they pass into second place when compared with colossal stars like Rigel and Betelgeuse. This suggests that the Sun with its dimensions and temperature, represents an average star; stars of its type are at least ten thousand times more common than ones such as Rigel.

Companions to Stars

There is, however, a common characteristic feature of stars which the Sun lacks: that is the presence of a companion. We live on a planet which circles around a single star and we find it strange to imagine two splendid stars rotating around a common centre of gravity at the centre of a planetary system; and yet this strange arrangement is very common and characteristic of the majority of stars. We have already cited Sirius and its companion and the Epsilon system in Auriga. There are many examples of situations more or less similar to be found in all parts of the cosmos. Sometimes a system includes four, five or six stars linked by gravitational attraction which ties them to complicated orbits. In these cases the apparent immobility of the universe is profoundly shaken. Even if the stellar orbits are enormous, telescopic observations reveal the movements produced by gravitation from one year to the next. Some double or triple stars are among the most marvellous objects one can observe. Their differences of temperature and other characteristics often create contrasting colours and different brightnesses which are splendid to see through the telescope.

In certain cases double stars are linked so closely in a physical system that no telescope can separate them; they are then separated by spectroscopic observations. Stars which revolve around others at such short distances that their atmospheres touch have been discovered. The motion of these pairs is so rapid that their revolutions are sometimes completed in a few days or so. In such cases, the mutual attraction deforms these stars and causes gigantic tidal phenomena. The components of the couples are no longer round but considerably flattened and their atmospheres are dispersed in space. When stars of this type have an orbit which coincides

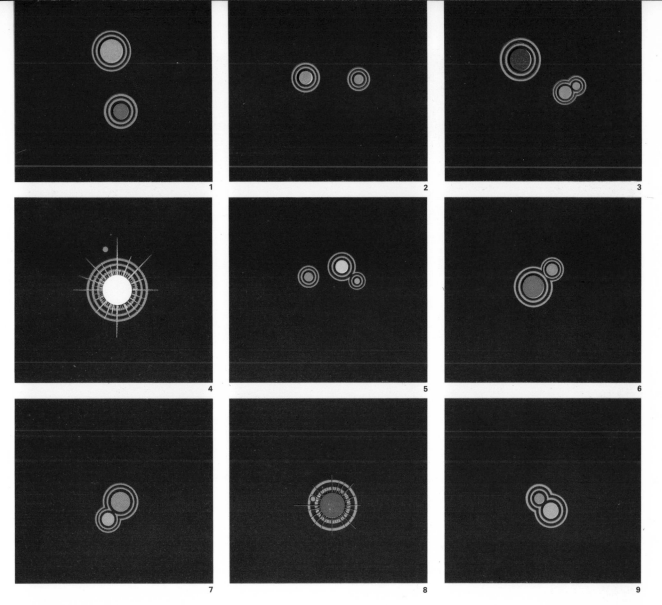

exactly with our visual plane (or if it is slightly displaced) one of the two stars periodically eclipses the other and the system which we see as a single star undergoes periodic variations in luminosity. These are the so-called 'eclipsing variables'; the most famous example in Algol, or Beta, in the constellation of Perseus with a period of less than three days. In Arabic Algol means 'the monster' or 'the devil'.

Extremely accurate measurements on the positions of the stars in the last decade have revealed that some have very slight movements which are the result of heavy bodies invisible both to the telescope and the spectroscope. Calculations based on the law of gravitation have demonstrated that these invisible companions of some stars have planetary type, not stellar, masses and that, therefore, they cannot emit light by the mass

luminosity relationship established by the English astronomer Sir Arthur Stanley Eddington (1882–1944). These invisible bodies are other planets, similar to those circulating around our Sun.

Extraordinary prospects are thus open to scientific research. Other worlds dragged along by the universal laws of gravitational attraction revolve around very remote suns; we cannot see them, but we know they exist. Perhaps on these globes life exists. Perhaps on these planets other thinking beings investigate the problems of the universe, as we do. We cannot say more, because all views of these planets are precluded, since they are submerged in the haloes of light from very remote stars; but their existence reveals new worlds and suggests too that mysterious secrets are hidden far beyond the darkness of the Earth's nights.

BIRTH AND DEATH OF THE STARS

Nebulae

In certain regions of the sky, against the dark background thronged with stars, the telescopes reveal mysterious objects like clouds moved by the wind. These cosmic clouds, called 'nebulae', present stupendous ranges of colour in photographs taken using the largest modern instruments. But the importance of nebulae goes far beyond the fact that they are fascinating objects to observe. They are the fundamental matter of creation, the spring from which the stars flow that populate the universe. Within nebulae the stars are born.

The nebulae are generally the points where the tenuous gas and the fine dust found everywhere in interstellar space condenses. The Earth is immersed in a mist of this material which is found in an extreme state of rarefication and which manifests itself only by producing a certain reddening of the most remote stars. This is a phenomenon similar to that which reddens the Sun at sunset. In these clouds there are only a few atoms in every cubic centimetre; the greatest vacuum which can be produced in terrestrial laboratories is millions of times denser. It has been calculated that in the nebulae the concentration of atoms is from ten to a thousand times greater than in the normal conditions in space. Still, the nebulae exist as extreme vacuums. Such are the beautiful, colourful cosmic clouds which are the gigantic laboratories where the radiant suns in the sky are first born.

The nebulae shine as the result of a luminescent phenomena caused by ultra-violet rays emanating from stars which are found within them or close to them. Sometimes the surrounding stars are not hot enough to provoke these coloured light emissions in the gas. If there is a sufficient quantity of dust particles, these shine by reflection. If, however, there is neither one nor the other phenomenon, because there are no stars nearby, the clouds remain obscure and are revealed only because they cause absolutely black patches in the sky, hiding the stars which lie beyond them. Light and dark clouds can be mixed in perspective, or when close together can create the appearance of a delicate embroidery of light and shade.

The most beautiful of the luminous clouds is without doubt the famous nebula in Orion which is visible to the naked eye because it forms the central star in the giant's sword. After what we have said about the constellations, it is easy to find the nebula of Orion. A pair of binoculars on a Moon-less night will reveal it clearly. In the big telescopes its appearance is astonishing; its delicate texture appears to be shaken by a tempestuous wind blowing from the depths of space. But there are no winds there, nor are the coloured clouds in any way equivalent to the clouds in our atmosphere. This extraordinary celestial object is at least 1,500 light-years from us. A ray from the stars which surround it takes thirty years to cross the nebula.

The nebula which surrounds the stars in the group of the Pleiades shines by reflection and shows a fine threadlike structure which differs from that seen in the great nebula of Orion. Other famous nebulae are North America in Cygnus, so-called because of its form, and the Trifid Nebula in Sagittarius. In both, bright and dark clouds alternate. In North America, a dark cloud forms the Gulf of Mexico and gives the nebula its shape.

Spectacular dark clouds can be seen around the star Zeta in Orion—the easterly one of the three which comprise the belt of the giant. The edge of this cosmic cloud is bordered by a silvery light from the stars which illuminate it from the other side of the cloud. From this shining edge, the outline

Left: *The great nebula in Orion, a gigantic but extremely tenuous cloud of gas which shines some 1,500 light-years from the Earth. The big telescopes reveal delicate moving structures and modern astronomical photography shows stupendous colourations in the nebula.*

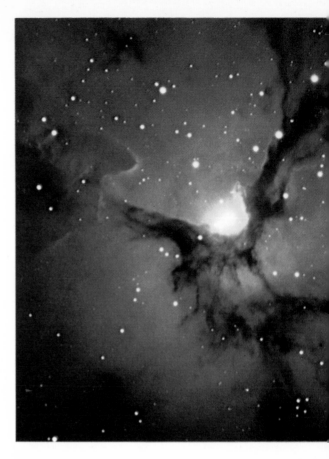

Above: *The dark nebula in the constellation of Orion is called the Horsehead Nebula.*

Centre: *The Trifid Nebula, so-called because of its shape, is in the constellation of Sagittarius.*

Opposite below: *The North America Nebula, in the constellation of Cygnus.*

of a contorted black cloud emerges. This is the famous Horsehead Nebula, called thus because of its shape. Even bigger clouds are seen with the naked eye in various parts of the Milky Way, where multitudes of stars are concealed.

Protostars

Nebulae are the birth places of stars. The matter of the clouds very slowly forms gigantic condensations which with the passage of millions of years separate into smaller denser masses, called 'protostars'. Differences of temperature and mutual attraction between the particles of the clouds, are responsible for this separation into isolated parts which continue to condense after formation. The cause of the contraction of the future stars is still obscure, but they generate high temperatures and pressures in their centres which, when they reach a certain point, cause nuclear reactions to start. Since cosmic matter is principally hydrogen, the reaction which occurs is the transformation of hydrogen into helium, as happens in the interior of the Sun. When the nuclear reactions

occur any isolated globe shines with bright light and it also radiates enormous quantities of energy.

From the protostar the true star is born, and starts its life as a luminous body. The creation of stars is continuous and we can witness it happening. In the great coloured clouds small dark globes can be seen, which in reality are hundreds or thousands of times more extensive than the entire Solar System. It has now been determined that from these, stars or groups of stars are born. We know, besides, of young stars which were born when the Earth was already old, or that have just been born.

Great Rigel has an age which, according to the latest calculations, cannot be more than ten million years. The Earth with the 6,000 million years which is now attributed to it is, in comparison, incredibly old. One of the stars in the southern constellation of Doradus is probably only 300,000 years old. Its light, in that case, appeared for the first time when Palaeolithic man first made his stone tools. Perhaps he, too, raised his eyes to the universe we are beginning to explore.

The presence of vortices in the nebulae produce rotational movements in the proto-stars, sometimes so rapidly as to sub-divide them, thus creating double stars or multiple systems. In other cases, a part of the primordial mass of dust and gas remains outside the part which becomes the single star and it forms a rotating belt which slowly breaks up into large vortices. In this turbulent cloud, the collisions in the eddying zones produce accumulations of material which increase slowly until they condense as the independent dark globes: the planets.

This mode of formation of the planetary systems was proposed in 1943 by the German astrophysicist C. von Weizsäcker for our Solar System. Almost two centuries before, the German philosopher Immanuel Kant (1724–1804) had expressed, even if in a vague form, an idea of much the same sort. The French mathematician Pierre Laplace elaborated on Kant's idea giving it a scientific form, and supposed that from the primordial solar cloud nebular rings had broken away which then condensed to form the planets. Laplace's theory was universally accepted in the last century; but when subjected to criticism, it was revealed as unacceptable.

In fact, the Sun revolves too slowly to have produced the breakaway of nebular rings in the distant past. Moreover, the rings would be stable, like those of Saturn, and incapable of condensing to form planets. Von Weizsäcker's theory eliminated these difficulties, especially after Gerard Kuiper had elaborated the theory by computation. Other new ideas are being proposed today which invoke the intervention of magnetic forces; but the essentials of the events described remain.

Observations have revealed the presence of invisible planets; and theory suggests that each star can form planets. We must deduce, therefore, that planetary systems are extremely common in the universe. This is one of the most disconcerting discoveries of modern astronomy.

A Star's Life

What happens, then, after a star is born and has formed a companion or a planetary

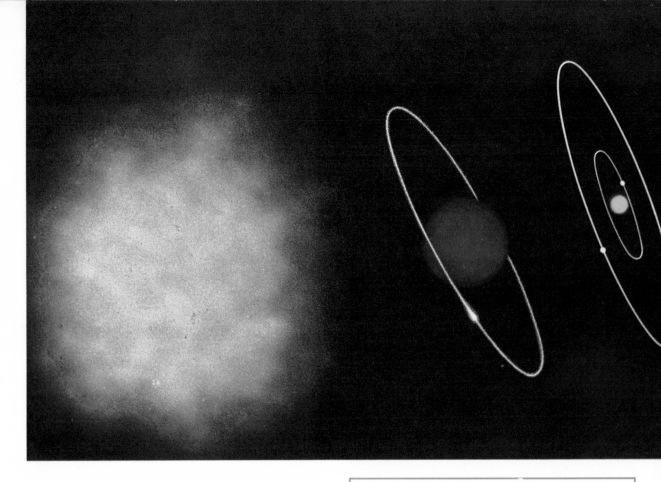

system? As an example, let us take an average star which is also the best known—the Sun. The events in its life will help illustrate the history of millions of other similar stars.

Theoretical astronomy suggests that the Sun is about 7,500 million years old. After the initial contraction, which probably lasted 25,000,000 years, the Sun started its hydrogen combustion phase and was not substantially changed. It shone on the first living organisms on Earth about 2,000 million years ago with the appearance it has today. However its luminosity is increasing very slowly and this process will continue without a break into the future, until the hydrogen situated in its centre is exhausted. Then, the Sun's evolution will assume a rapid rhythm, and this will come about in approximately 5,000 million years. Our star will probably become larger and brighter, and as it swells it will cool off until it becomes a red giant. Its enormous tenuous chromosphere will engulf Mercury, then Venus and perhaps even the Earth. But when the red tangle of its prominences reaches our planet, there will be nothing to consume but a burnt rock; because long before, the increase in light and heat will destroy all living things.

Later still the red giant will disappear from the scene. The Sun will become deflated and unstable; thermonuclear reactions may be established in its interior which differ from the normal hydrogen-helium reactions, and perhaps even an explosion could take place. In the end nothing will remain but a ruin. All its matter will collapse around its centre and assume the degenerate state which we have found in the companion of Sirius. The Sun will become a white dwarf, a dead star, surrounded by dead worlds. But because creation continues all around, there will be new heavens and new earths.

The Sun is typical and represents, as we have said, the average star. Smaller stars can have a much longer life and last, it is thought,

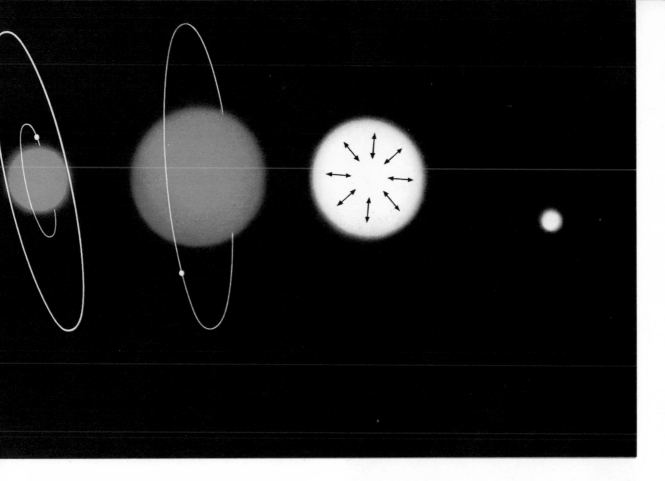

even more than a hundred thousand million years. On the other hand, the large luminous stars, like the blue giants, have a much shorter life. Their energy dispersal is too high for them to have a long life. It has been calculated that the very luminous stars have a probable duration of 10,000,000 years or even as little as 500,000 years. Innumerable stars of this type were born, have lived and died during geological time, as we reckon it.

Variable Stars

In some stars of various ages certain oscillations of light and temperature have been observed which denote particular conditions in their interiors. These are the so-called 'variable stars' which change more or less rhythmically with periods which range from a few days (even a few hours) to several months or several years. It is certain that the nuclear reactions which furnish these stars with energy are subjected to unexpected renewal followed by slackening. The cause of this phenomenon is however obscure. The most famous of the variables are the Cepheids which take their name from the star Delta Cephei, the first of their type observed. The Cepheids are pulsating stars; their globes

dilate and contract periodically with profound rhythmical variations in their superficial temperatures and physical conditions. Scientists are closely observing these stars to find out more about them.

Associated with the variables are stars of an even more extraordinary character than the pulsating stars: these are the cataclysmic variables. Although this latter group comprises various types of stars, its principal representatives are those called in Latin 'novae' and 'supernovae'. Novae are stars which suddenly, in the space of a few hours, become tens of thousands of times brighter than normal; they have a sort of explosion which affects the photosphere, but not the interior. The explosion is followed by contraction while the star slowly diminishes in brightness. The expelled gas is dispersed in space at a velocity which ranges from 2,000 to 3,000 kilometres (1,240 to 1,860 miles) per second. In a supernova the brightness increases until it shines like a thousand million suns; this phenomenon occurs in a few hours. It has been calculated that these stars, in the three months following an explosion, liberate as much energy as the Sun radiates in 500,000,000 years! Compared to the

explosion of a supernova, the explosion of a nova is rather like a modest firework.

These cataclysms mark, practically, the last phase in the life of a star and precede by only a short time (in the cosmic time scale, of course) the white dwarf stage. It is not clearly known what nuclear reaction produces these stages, although various hypotheses have been advanced. It is possible, however, that the Sun itself must pass through the nova state, after it has dilated as a red giant, and after it has assumed an aspect similar to certain pulsating variables.

Various nebulae, rounded in shape or in the form of rings, represent the remains of supernovae which have exploded in the past and in which the gas continues to expand in space. In the constellation of Taurus a characteristic nebula exists, with contorted filaments around the edges which have given rise to it being called the Crab Nebula. At the point where it shines Chinese astronomers in 1054 observed something they thought was a new star and which we now know as the 'Supernova of 1054'. Its gas, animated by violent turbulence, continues to spread from its centre and constitutes a powerful source of radio waves. Similarly, a very powerful radio wave source exists in the constellation of Cassiopeia, where in 1572 a celebrated supernova exploded. This was Tycho's Star, named after Tycho Brahe who studied it. However, here the nebulosity of Tycho's Star is absent and this renders its identification as a supernova doubtful. A typical case however, is to be found in the filamentous nebula of Cygnus, a gaseous ring with a diameter of 300 million million million (trillion) kilometres ($186\frac{1}{2}$ trillion miles). It has been calculated that the supernova which gave rise to this exploded about 20,000 years ago.

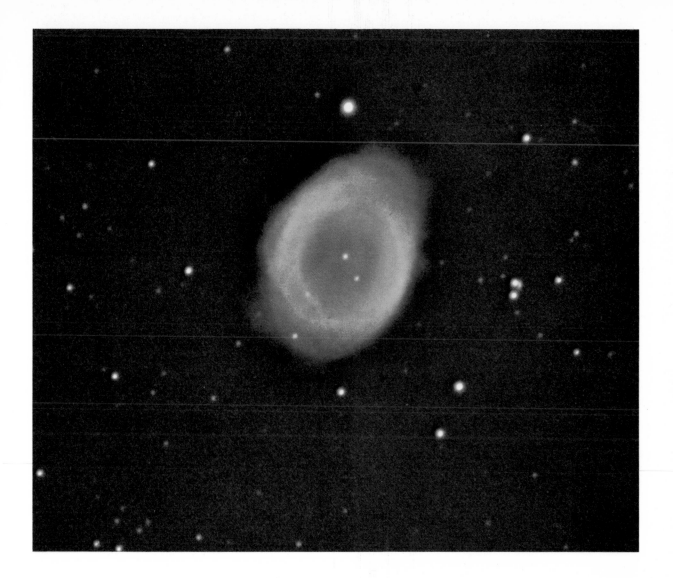

More than three hundred nebulae are known, some spheroidal, some 'planetary' or annular shaped, and some hundreds of times more extensive than our Solar System. One of the most beautiful is the Annular Nebula in Lyra, which is seen as a marvellously coloured ring in photographs.

Between cosmic death and life there is a close connection, because the gas expelled in the stellar explosions goes to be added to the cosmic matter from which new blazing stars appear. Thus the stellar cycle starts again where it ends, in one prodigious renewal.

Cosmogony

Study of the birth and death of the stars is one of the ways in which astronomers peer into the future. We want to know exactly how old the Earth is as a planet and exactly how it was formed. And, we also want to know the ages of the stars, the galaxies and the whole universe and how it was formed. *Cosmogony* is the branch of theoretical astronomy which deals with all of these questions. Since very ancient times, this area of research has produced many fascinating theories, but so far none have been proven beyond a shadow of a doubt. However, today astronomers are certainly getting closer to the answers.

Within the past thirty years or so, three groups of facts have been established upon which modern theories are based. These facts are: (1) the universe is expanding; (2) there is a preponderance of hydrogen, the simplest of the elements, in stars and in interstellar matter; (3) energy is radiated by the stars and plays a definite role in nuclear reactions occurring. These ideas are all leading men of science into a more concrete conception of the past and the future of our universe.

THE GALAXY, A CLOUD OF SUNS

One night long ago in 1845, Lord Rosse, Count of Parsonstown in Ireland, was exploring the sky with a big telescope which he had installed at his own expense in his castle. Fascinated by astronomy, he spent a fortune constructing an instrument which was better than others existing at the time. In his first trial experiment Lord Rosse discovered unexpected marvels. The slow rotation of the starry vault carried into the field of his instrument a pale nebula which the Frenchman Charles Messier, in his catalogue of nebulae in 1730, had given the number 51 (M51). Then Lord Rosse saw something which no other man had ever seen: a great silver spiral outlined against the black depths of the sky, perfectly analogous, in spite of its immobility, to a Catherine-wheel firework. The news of his discovery was received with both admiration and doubts. Even so, some astronomers thought that the spiral of stars was an enormous remote system similar to the Milky Way in which the Earth is immersed. This supposition was correct although many decades passed before it was confirmed by other scientists and astronomers.

Hitherto we have encountered, in the nebulae category, gas and dust; but there are stellar systems which are also composed of gas and dust. Tenuous clouds relatively close to Earth, or stellar accumulations dispersed in the most profound depths of the cosmos, can produce in the telescope at first sight the same appearance as some nebulae. Charles Messier, with the aid of a modest telescope, produced a list of gas clouds, groups of stars (stellar clusters) and gigantic stellar systems. His list comprised 103 'objects'. A century later in 1890 J. L. E. Dreyer published the *New General Catalogue* which increased the list to 7,840 celestial objects of different types. Even today these objects carry numbers from one of the two catalogues, the letter M for Messier's, or NGC for Dreyer's. Only in relatively recent times has it been possible to determine the distances and the types of these celestial objects.

Since Lord Rosse's time, M51 has been repeatedly photographed, and modern photographic techniques have obtained very fine images, even in colour. A look at these photographs sets one thinking: we see in them a perfect reproduction in plane view of what is considered to be our galaxy, at a distance which is almost inconceivable. However, the galaxy populated by stars in which we live and which somehow seems boundless is in reality a gigantic spiral constellation of hundreds of millions of stars. Its

Left: *The name of the Milky Way comes from Greek mythology: when the Goddess Juno fed the baby Hercules, a drop of milk fell from her breast and spread through the sky leaving a bright white band across the starry firmament.*

Opposite page: *The spiral galaxy M51 in the constellation of the Hunting Dogs. This is a system composed of thousands of millions of stars similar to our own galaxy.*

form has only been revealed in recent years. The true, great universe is composed of an endless number of similar isolated systems. It was thought up to a few decades ago that by increasing the power of astronomical instruments, there would be an infinite increase in the number of visible stars. However there were persons who had intuitively guessed the structure of the cosmos as we know it today; but their voices remained unheard because astronomy techniques long ago did not allow their hypotheses to be checked.

In the mid-eighteenth century ideas similar to those held today were expressed by the Englishman Thomas Wright and the German philosopher Immanual Kant accepted them with enthusiasm. But it was only in the period from 1922 to 1924, after the great telescope at Mount Wilson came into use (it has an objective mirror with a diameter of 2½ metres or 100 inches), that the separation of the great universe into distinct systems, which were called 'island universes', was finally clarified by two American astronomers E. Hubble and M. Humason. The cosmos then assumed real dimensions and a new structure which men had never expected.

Now, the expression 'island universe' is no longer used. The universe is considered the total of all the celestial bodies at whatever distance they are and in whatever system they occur. Thus the galaxy in which we live, the Milky Way, is only a drop in an ocean of many other galaxies.

The Shape of the Galaxy

We can define the galaxy in which our Sun is situated more or less precisely. It comprises about one hundred thousand million suns, and a quantity of gas and cosmic dust two-and-a-half times more than the mass of all the stars combined. It is flattened like a disc, but inflated at the centre, and it extends its gigantic spiral arms in space like a huge Catherine-wheel, which rotates around its axis taking millions of years and which moves towards unknown regions in space. A ray of light takes a hundred thousand years to cross our galaxy. It has been calculated that to measure its

diameter with thread from a spider's web, fifty thousand million tons of this fine thread would be needed. Our radiant Sun, in this prodigious system, is little more than a lost spark, in much the same way as a bright dust speck dances among innumerable others in a ray of light entering a darkened room. The Sun is 30,000 light-years distant from the galactic centre and circles around it in 220 million years. Now the Sun has returned to the point in its orbit which it occupied when the forests of the Carboniferous period grew on the Earth, long before the first appearance of the prehistoric dinosaurs. The lifetime of the entire human race, compared with such an immense period of time, has no significance at all.

Our galaxy takes its name from the Milky Way, the white band which shines from horizon to horizon across the sky. Many ancient philosophers thought that it was the point where the two celestial hemispheres were welded together. The cloud of suns which comprises the Milky Way awaited the telescope to be revealed to man. The first weak telescopes made by Galileo were enough to demonstrate innumerable stars, but they were too faint and close together to

appear separate.

In the big telescopes, the dense regions of the Milky Way are revealed as prodigious accumulations of stars. Between them, the same distances intervene which we already know separate the stars shining in the constellations. Since we are situated in the plane of the galactic disc, the view from Earth shows star upon star without end in the direction of the plane.

Among these stars are endless groups of globes of the same type as our Sun, and also very luminous giants and super giants. Nevertheless, the enormous distances hide them from our eyes and they only appear as a pale silvery river which even the most tenuous night mist can obliterate.

All the stars which we see indistinctly form part of the Milky Way, which is our galaxy. It is not difficult to understand the reason why the stars seem separate and independent. If we suppose we are in a field early in the morning, and a transient layer of mist forms which does not reach the tops of the trees, then we see all around us an opaque ring; but the minute droplets of water in the vertical thickness of the mist are sufficiently rarefied to reveal the blue of the sky. The stars are exactly like the droplets in this mist: all around us they form a ring, the Milky Way. Above and below this ring, the black sky is revealed because the stars are widely spaced.

Let us now look at the mythical track of the Sun's chariot: before our eyes the galactic system slowly takes shape with an unforeseen clarity. In the night sky beyond the splendours of Orion, the Milky Way is faint; in that direction we are looking towards the edge of the system. In the summer sky the Milky Way is a luminous river of light especially beyond the stars in Sagittarius; and there lies the centre of the galaxy.

Yet, we can extend our observation beyond this. On summer nights the great cross of Cygnus passes high over our heads and it is easy to see that the Milky Way divides in that area into two distinct branches: a larger one points towards Sagittarius, and a weaker one extends towards Scorpio. Between the two branches, the sky appears particularly empty, and forms an irregular black streak which is lost beyond the horizon. This streak is not a gap in the galaxy; it is a clear view of large accumulations of cosmic dust and obscure gas which occur in the galactic plane and which hide the luminous centre. If we are aware that the black cosmic river is nearer to Earth than the galactic brightness then the two separate branches of the galaxy fade from our view and we clearly see the enormous disc of the galaxy, inflated at its centre, with the groups of dark nebulae suspended in space between the Sun and the constellation of Sagittarius.

Beyond Sagittarius, at a distance of 30,000 light-years from us, the galaxy forms a sort of bulb or inflated lens which is 20,000 light-years wide in its thickest part. In this central inflation, gas and dust are absent. The marvellous bright nebulae, together with

On the right *in the foreground is shown the para- boloid of the radio telescope* Mark I *which weighs 800 tons. With this radio telescope, which is in use at the English astronomical observatory at Jodrell Bank, it is possible to follow space probes for enormous distances. This, however, was not the principal activity for which this marvellous instrument was designed. In fact, with it man tries to extend his knowledge of the universe beyond the limits imposed by normal light telescopes and also to investigate those regions of the universe from which no light comes, but which certainly are not empty of stars. A project which foresees the use of 36 radio telescopes, organised in such a way as to function like a single gigantic radio telescope, is that illustrated in the diagram below. The project has the name V.L.A. (initials for Very Large Array), and it is sponsored by the National Radioastronomical Observatory of America (N.R.A.O.). The project involves the construction of a group of 36 parabolic aerials each of 25 metres (approximately 820 feet) in diameter, dispersed on three tracks built at 120° to one another which would form a circle with a diameter of 42 kilometres (approximately 26 miles). This system should increase by one thousand times the signals from any one cosmic source; in other words, the listening complex, V.L.A., would be one thousand times more powerful than the most powerful radio telescope now in use.*

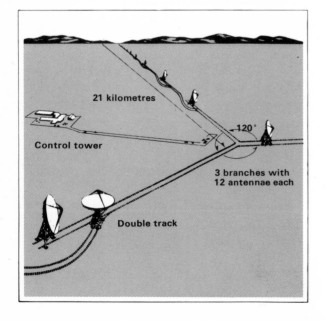

21 kilometres

Control tower

120°

3 branches with 12 antennae each

Double track

the clouds which cut dark gaps through the splendour of the stars extend all along the rays of the great galactic wheel. Thus, in the spiral-shaped arms splendid blue stars blaze continually, while in the central bulb, only very old stars shine and they move towards extinction without the possibility of substitution by new stars.

Star Clusters

Astronomers distinguish two categories of stars, those of the arms and those of the nucleus of the galaxy by the names 'Population I' and 'Population II'. This is the work of the American astronomer Walter Baade who established this difference in 1944; his discovery is now considered fundamental. If we could stand in extra-galactic space and admire the tremendous pinwheel in which our Sun is found, we would see a blue colour in the arms where the young stars blaze and a reddish colouration in the nucleus itself where the Population II stars include red giants and old stars. Similar appearances are clearly visible in many stellar systems beyond our own. Our Sun is on the edge of one of the arms of the great spiral and forms part of a group of stars called the 'Local Cluster'. It

Above: *The development of the Milky Way in the sky, with its dense parts and its dark clouds. This map has been drawn taking the plane of the Milky Way as the equator.* Left: *The galaxy as it would appear from above.*

Below: *The galaxy seen in cross section with the position of the Sun indicated on the right.*

seems strange to call a group of suns which are many light-years apart a cluster; however, they have movements in common and have the same origin. The Local Cluster is similar to that of the Hyades in Taurus. Other clusters with stars much closer together are scattered around us. A typical one is the Pleiades, which in the telescope appears as a cloud of stars accompanied by bright dust. The Pleiades is clearly visible to the naked eye. People with normal vision can usually see about six or seven stars in the cluster, while those with extremely good vision can see ten, or even twelve or fourteen without a telescope. Much more remote than the Pleiades, the cluster called The Crib in Cancer and the double cluster Persei (which appears as two faint patches of milky light in the region between Cassiopeia and Perseus) are seen with the naked eye only as dim stars; in the telescopes they appear like handfuls of diamonds.

Since the galaxy rotates with unequal velocity, faster near the centre and more slowly farther out, the clusters tend to move apart even if very slowly. The breakup of vast stellar associations is much more rapid. Thus the appearance of the sky is modified over a period of time. The starry vault which shone in the Paleolithic period is no longer quite the same as the one we contemplate. Two and a half centuries ago, the astronomer Edmund Halley noted that certain stars did not occupy the positions indicated in Ptolemy's catalogue. Now that we understand the movements of a number of stars, we know that in 100,000 years many constellations with which we are familiar today will be greatly deformed, and that in a million years they will be quite unrecognisable.

Thus everything moves around us in a universe which is evolving endlessly. Hundreds and hundreds of groups of stars, born in the prodigious cosmic clouds, continually disappear in the galactic spiral, while others are ready to replace them.

Only the so-called 'globular' clusters are not subjected to the continual change which deforms the arms of our system; this happens because globular clusters are situated above

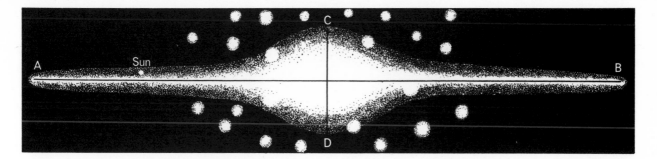

Above: *A diagram showing the Milky Way galaxy in plane view. The Sun is shown to the left of the centre; A to B is equal to 100,000 light-years and C to D is equal to about 20,000 light-years.*

and below the plane of the galaxy away from the currents of stars and cosmic matter.

Currently, about one hundred and twenty globular clusters have been discovered. Twelve of these are very faint and, therefore, probably lie outside our galaxy and should be classified as intergalactic objects. Most of these clusters were known to Herschel in the mid-18th century, and because very few have been discovered since then—despite the increase in powerful telescopes—it seems reasonable to assume that these objects are unevenly distributed throughout the starry skies.

The finest of these clusters is M13 in Messier's catalogue which is seen in the constellation Hercules, but it is extraordinarily more remote than the stars which form the mythical hero. To the naked eye, or in binoculars, M13 seems to be a diffuse star; but in a large telescope it is a prodigious globe of stars, so condensed at its centre that it is impossible to see them separately. The spectacle of this sphere of very distant suns, shimmering within the field of the telescope as a result of our atmosphere, is one of the most beautiful that astronomy can offer.

An abyss of 34,000 light-years separates this celestial marvel from the Earth. In that abyss the stars are much closer together than are the stars in space near us; their average

distance apart is about a light-year, and about 100,000 stars form the cluster. Since there is no cosmic material between them to form new stars, they are all Population II stars. Over a hundred clusters like this are known, all similar and all remote, linked by their origin to the galactic system and dragged along by its rotation, but all moving outside the great spiral. Dispersed around the galaxy in space devoid of stars and gas, these star clusters form a gigantic aureole around our own system.

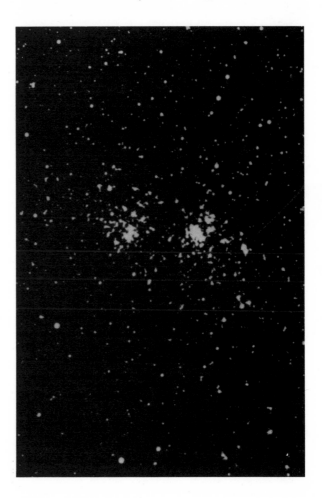

Right: *The double cluster in Perseus photographed at Yerkes Observatory, Williams Bay, Wisconsin, U.S.A.*

Opposite page: *The marvellous globular cluster in the constellation of Hercules, taken at Mount Palomar, California.*

147

THE INFINITE UNIVERSE

The Abyss of Space

Accompanied by its swarm of globular clusters, the gigantic Milky Way galaxy rotates in space. Around it the abysses of the greatest vacuum that the mind of man can imagine open wide. Similar galaxies rotate beyond these abysses, separated from each other by spaces equally as great. Millions of suns are dragged along in their vortices. If we could be carried miraculously into intergalactic space, hundreds of thousands of light-years from our system, we would see around us profound blackness, broken only by faint luminous specks produced by the nearest galaxies. All the splendours of the night sky would be forgotten because space is populated by great galactic systems not by stars.

A stupendous galaxy shines in the constellation of Andromeda close enough to be seen with the naked eye. This is the famous M31 which is revealed as an enormous system seen almost in cross-section; it appears as an elongated ellipse. In autumn nights when Andromeda and Pegasus appear above our heads as does the Plough or Great Bear it is easy to see M31. If a line is traced from the Pole Star through the western half of the 'W' of Cassiopeia, before reaching the stars in Andromeda, the line will encounter a faintly luminous object like a dull star. There lies the best-known galaxy in the sky.

The enormous distances which we have encountered so far lose all meaning when compared with that of the galaxy in Andromeda. However, large telescopes enable us to study the galaxy in all its particulars. In photographs we can easily see the reddish central nucleus composed of stars of Population II and around it the elegant spirals with Population I stars which give them a bluish tint. In the arms of the spiral great chains of dark clouds unroll and other irregular dark clouds indicate the limit of the brilliant nucleus. Everything there seems to reproduce our own galaxy.

In M31 variable stars have been studied (which have enabled us to determine the distance of the galaxy from ours) together with open clusters and globular clusters. The explosion of novae and the even more enormous explosions of supernovae have been observed also. The only difference between the Andromeda galaxy and our system is that M31 is bigger. The frighteningly large scale of distances found in our galaxy is still greater in M31 and consequently the number of stars and clusters is greater. While we are surrounded by about 100 globular clusters, there is a swarm of about 200 around the galaxy in Andromeda. If there were inhabitants on a planet in M31 situated in a position corresponding to that which Earth occupies in our galaxy, they would see a 'Milky Way' in their sky in much the same way as that which shines during our clear nights. If we found ourselves there we would see new and unknown constellations; but, overall, the starry vault around a planet in M31 would not appear very different from the sky around Earth.

The Shapes of Galaxies

We have already mentioned another spiral, M51 in the constellation of the Hunting Dogs, which is always seen in plane view. Other spirals can be seen from the side and we can observe them in perfect profile with the nucleus and the dark layers of gas and cosmic matter situated in their plane of rotation. Studies made with the great telescope at Mount Wilson Observatory have shown that spirals have a structure of a Catherine-wheel type firework with two single arms which extend from opposite sides of the nucleus and which then increase in length, follow each other and branch out. It is thought that these arms are produced by gigantic magnetic fields. This would explain why particular spirals, such as the 'barred'

The illustration opposite shows how a great spiral galaxy appears when seen in profile.

The great spiral nebula in the constellation Andromeda which is two million light years distant from the Milky Way. In many ways the Andromeda Nebula is a galaxy similar to ours, so much so that many astronomers have called it our 'twin'. The first astronomers to discover that nebulae are gigantic masses of stars were the Americans Edwin P. Hubble and Milton Humason in 1922. The nebula in Andromeda—in scientific terminology M31—is the only extra-galactic (outside the galaxy) nebula visible to the naked eye. In 1948-49 the central nucleus and the arms of the nebula were resolved into stars; moreover, the presence of about 200 globular clusters similar to those existing around our galaxy were recognised. The number of galaxies which have been recognised and catalogued during the last two centuries amounts to more than 12,000.

type, have a nucleus at the centre of a sort of rectilinear bar which is then prolonged at its extremities in two arms.

Not all the galaxies have this shape. There are elliptical ones in which there is no trace of a spiral form, nor any layer of dark clouds. There are also irregular galaxies without a defined stellar distribution. Up to a few years ago, it was thought that the great spirals were born in the elliptical galaxies which had been flattened and had branched out as a result of the rotation. Then, it was established that the elliptical galaxies abounded in Population II stars; therefore, an evolution in this sense was not possible. Perhaps some elliptical galaxies are the remains of great spirals which consumed all the primary matter which produced the stars in the arms. Perhaps, too, each type of galaxy has undergone an independent evolution tied to the quantity—large or small—of gas and dust which it possessed initially.

The Dimensions of Galaxies

The dimensions of the stellar systems vary as do the types. In 1965, the research astronomer W. Morgan at Mount Palomar revealed that the galaxy NGC 6166 is very much bigger than M31 in Andromeda; perhaps even more than four times larger and brighter. NGC 6166 is an enormous galaxy; many others, however, are much smaller than ours and some can be called dwarfs. These are then found as satellites around the bigger ones. A typical example is the Magellanic Clouds; two bright spots which stand out in the southern sky, not far from the Milky Way, which were named by the first navigators who ventured into the unknown southern seas. The larger of the two, the Greater Magellanic Cloud, with all its stars, clusters and interstellar matter, emits light equal to one-third of that which emanates from the galaxy. The lesser Magellanic Cloud is at least three times smaller.

Top of the opposite page: *Two galaxies which show the principal types of spiral. On the left: a normal spiral; on the right: a barred spiral.*

Above: *In remote galaxies we observe the explosions of supernovae which stand out because of their brightness. This is equivalent to thousands of millions of stars. In the picture, a supernova which appeared in the galaxy NGC 1073 photographed at Asiago Observatory, Padua, Italy. On the right is the central part of the galaxy; on the left is the supernova.*

Bottom, opposite page: *The galaxy NGC 153 in the constellation of the Sculptor forms part of the Local Group (which includes the Milky Way and the Andromeda nebula) and is one of the closest galaxies to our own (460,000 light-years away).*

Below: *The beautiful spiral M33 in the constellation of the Triangulum is one of the most remote in the Local Group, which comprises star systems up to 3,000,000 light-years away.*

The Magellanic Clouds are from 120,000 to 190,000 light years away. Visibility of the spiral structure of the larger one is poor because it is masked by intervening interstellar matter. The smaller one is an irregular galaxy. The Magellanic Clouds are important because they formed the first bridge between the Earth and the distances of the extra-galactic nebula. In fact, the Cepheid variables which pulsate in the Lesser Magellanic Cloud enabled the American astronomer Henrietta Swan Leavitt in 1913, at Harvard College Observatory, to make the discovery of a relationship between the period and the brightness of these stars which then served as a means of measuring the abyss which separates us from the galaxy in Andromeda. After this important leap forward, more precise results were obtained in 1952 at Mount Palomar and the way was opened to accurate measurements of the cosmos.

The Magellanic Clouds are linked to our galaxy by bridges of matter revealed by radio astronomical measurements. But these are not the only galaxies joined to the destiny of our galaxy. Ours is to be found in a real cluster of galaxies called the Local Group comprising about twenty stellar systems distributed in a sphere with a radius of 3,000,000 light-years. The largest of these is the galaxy in Andromeda, which is also accompanied by small satellite galaxies; ours is the second largest in size. All these 'island universes' are linked by gravity and rotate around an unknown centre situated between the Milky Way and Andromeda.

Infinite Galaxies

Like the stars, the galaxies tend to be united in clusters, creating super systems of an inconceivable size. The universe has many of these clusters, sometimes extraordinarily diffuse, and separated by prodigious distances. If we leave the Local Group, we would have to travel for 30,000,000 years at the speed of light to reach the closest cluster, in the constellation of Virgo. There thousands of galaxies radiate light. When we photograph them we record their very remote past. Modern astronomical instruments continue to enable man to discover new and even more remote stellar systems. In the

Astronomical Classification of Galaxies:
The small diagram at the top left *and the photograph on the* right *joined by red lines give a clear idea of the astronomical classification of the galaxies according to their structure. In the small diagram, the three galaxies along the upper red line are circular, elliptical and lenticular; the three along the left-hand red line are normal spirals; and the three along the right-hand line are barred spirals.*

On the right-hand side this scheme is shown in enlarged form as a series of actual photographs.

Astronomers once thought that the evolutionary development of galaxies occurred as shown in the small illustration from top to bottom, that is from the circular shape to the barred spiral. However, they now believe galaxies evolve in the opposite way (See diagram, p. 158).

Examples represented in the small diagram (enlarged on right) are: top—nebula NGC 3379, a circular nebula; third from top— nebula NGC 3115, a lenticular nebula which closely resembles the illustration. Left-hand branch *of diagram: top—NGC 4594 closely resembles the illustration; middle—M31 in Andromeda and M81 in Ursa Major (the Great Bear) closely resemble the illustration; bottom—M101 in Ursa Major and M33 in Triangulum closely resemble the illustration. All three examples in the left-hand branch are normal spirals.* Right-hand branch *of diagram: these are all examples of barred spirals. Top— NGC 2859, a spiral with short bars; middle— NGC 5850, a spiral with more prominent recurved bars; bottom—NGC 7479, a spiral with well-developed bars.*

Only one of these galaxies, M31 in Andromeda, is just visible under ideal conditions to the naked eye.

depths of the cosmos endless galaxies shine with faint lights. In an area of the sky as large as the Moon's disc it has been calculated that on average 400 galaxies can be found. Thus, in the whole sky, there are approximately 1,000 million galaxies which can be photographed with a telescope like the one at Mount Palomar or from which radio waves can be detected with the biggest radio telescopes.

The Sun in our great galaxy has been likened to a grain of dust in a ray of light. This comparison applies not only to the Sun but to the galaxy itself. A question emerges from this discussion: if the planets around the Sun are a common phenomenon, how many planets are there in a universe of galaxies where each one of these involves thousands of millions of stars? The sky unfolds fantastic stellar systems unknown to our predecessors. But, the ancient problem of whether life exists on other worlds similar to the Earth is still puzzling.

Innumerable galaxies shine in the black abysses of the cosmos. Some of these suddenly reveal the prodigious flashes of supernovae. Others are in contact with their neighbours creating phenomena which unleash emissions of radio waves of unimaginable intensity. Still others reveal indescribable cataclysmic explosions which destroy entire clusters of stars at once. In the luminous nucleus of each galaxy there is always a small bright central point which is really an accumulation of millions of stars very close together; within that point a supernova can provoke a chain reaction of explosions of hundreds of supernovae. A phenomenon of this sort was discovered for the first time a few years ago at Mount Palomar in the galaxy M82, which shines faintly 10,000,000 light-years from the Earth in the constellation of the Great Bear. Before that discovery, the occurrence of such a thing had not been even imagined.

Galaxies and 'Time'

All this phenomenal activity takes place around us, but to use the phrase 'takes place' is inaccurate because the 'present' which is imprinted on photographic plates is really the 'past' of the cosmos. A cluster of galaxies

Above: *Galaxies in the great constellation of Hercules.*

Opposite page: *A diagram of certain galaxies with their relative distances and recessional velocities: the latter is obtained by measuring the red shift of the spectral lines emitted by them.*

Velocity of recession of certain nebulae

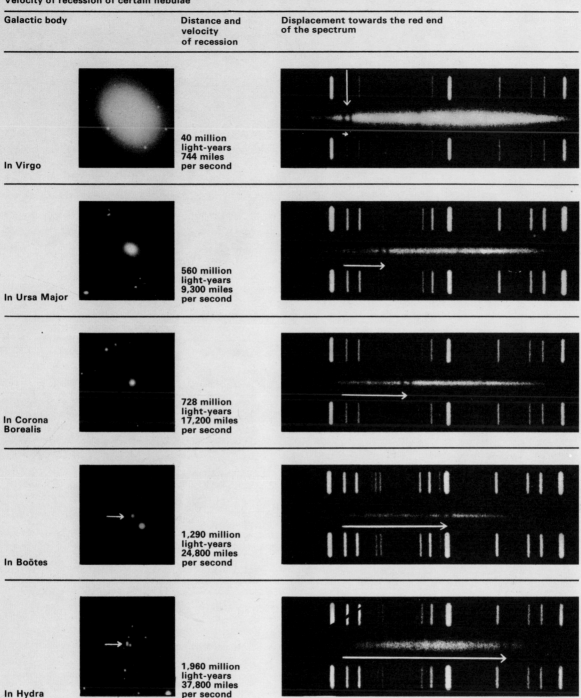

Galactic body	Distance and velocity of recession	Displacement towards the red end of the spectrum
In Virgo	40 million light-years 744 miles per second	
In Ursa Major	560 million light-years 9,300 miles per second	
In Corona Borealis	728 million light-years 17,200 miles per second	
In Boötes	1,290 million light-years 24,800 miles per second	
In Hydra	1,960 million light-years 37,800 miles per second	

in the constellation of Coma Berenices is 300,000,000 light-years away; another in the Corona Borealis composed of hundreds of members shines 900,000,000 light-years from us. These are stupefying examples of distance, but in stellar terms these clusters are still relatively near to us. The great eyes of the telescopes penetrate much deeper into space and time. The Mount Palomar telescope has photographed a group of several hundred galaxies in Hydra from which the light set out 2,600 million years ago.

The Earth, with its fossils, has revealed times which are enormously remote. Geology has shown that the massive Brontosaurus grazed in the Jurassic lagoons 180 million years ago and that the first reptiles impressed their footsteps in the mud among the enormous ferns 270 million years ago. The science of astronomy demands an awareness

157

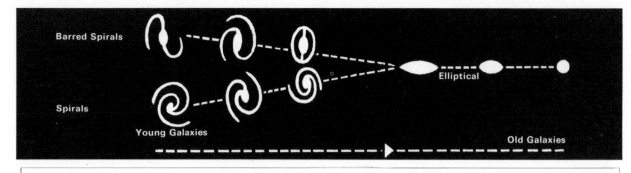

Barred Spirals

Spirals

Elliptical

Young Galaxies

Old Galaxies

This diagram shows the evolution of galaxies, from left to right.

of even greater time and distance. The most remote observable galaxy, which is called 3C-275 is 6,000 million light-years away from the Earth. Astronomers photograph it now as it existed before the Earth was created, when the Sun itself was not even born.

However, galaxy 3C-275 does not touch the observable limits of the universe which surrounds us. Surpassing the colossal optical instruments, powerful radio telescopes carry us far beyond galaxy 3C-275. Galaxies of the 3C-275 type are powerful sources of radio waves, but have an observable extension. Other sources of radio waves equally as strong are apparently of almost inestimable size and in numerous cases the giant telescope at Mount Palomar cannot succeed in providing even an image in the form of a faint point of light. These surprising stars are called quasi-stellar radio sources (or quasars). Up to a few years ago no one even suspected their existence. It was in 1961 that radio telescopes first picked up very strong radio sources which could not be associated with any photographs taken even with the very largest telescopes. After more study scientists found that these radio sources could be linked with objects that looked like stars, but that did not act like ordinary ones. One possible explanation for them is that they are the products of the explosions of central regions of gigantic galaxies. Their radio waves have travelled, in some cases, for 10,000 million years, perhaps even 15,000 million years, before being detected on Earth.

One of the most recent theories suggests that quasars may have a dense core of millions of suns which pulsates every few years. These pulsations then emit shock waves which increase as they travel outwards and finally reach us many times increased. The

real nature of quasars poses many difficult problems for cosmogony, but research on them continues and eventually scientists may know enough about them to determine what they are composed of and how they radiate radio waves.

Having arrived at the limit of present-day knowledge, we glimpse new horizons awaiting exploration. Slowly and with difficulty astronomy seeks to arrive at a precise concept of the universe, but the limits still escape science. Since 1929 we have known that the galaxies are moving away from one another and various theoretical models of the universe have been studied in a search to understand these phenomena. The possibility of testing theoretical studies by observations has been outlined, but still many years of scientific study are required.

The Expansion of the Universe

The reciprocal separation of the galaxies, 'the expansion of the universe' as it has come to be known popularly, is studied from the luminous messages which come to us from distant systems. As the molecules of a puff of smoke disperse in the air, the galaxies disperse in space. Their faint spectra which reveal Fraunhofer lines tell us this. These lines are all displaced towards the red end of the spectrum, and the farther a galaxy is away the greater the displacement. As a well-known physical principal, this displacement indicates a separation from us, a 'recession' as it is called in astronomy, which can be measured. We thus find flight at an ever increasing velocity. While the galaxies 40,000,000 light-years away depart at a speed of 1,200 kilometres (746 miles) per second those in the Corona cluster at 900,000,000 light-years depart at a speed of

21,600 kilometres (13,422 miles) per second. The very remote systems in Hydra disappear into the cosmos at still higher velocities, some at 61,000 kilometres (37,900 miles) a second.

The mysterious quasars behave the same as the galaxies and speed towards the spatial abyss at much greater velocities. Our galaxy is not in a central position from which all other galaxies are fleeing

Our great spiral is not the centre of the universe any more than the Earth is. Space expands, dragging the galaxies with it. Attempts have been made to explain the displacement of the lines of the spectrum in other ways, so far without satisfactory results, but work and discussion continues. The expansion of the universe implies a past, extremely remote, when the galaxies were very close together. Some enormous phenomenon probably occurred then. Perhaps it was the creation? But it is premature to affirm this. Around 15,000 million years ago there may have been a beginning to something which has developed up to the present state of the universe. But was it a beginning, a cosmic creation, or was it a renewal?

Our brief journey through the sky is now more or less completed. Astronomers are continually studying not only our Milky Way Galaxy but the galaxies and other stellar systems which exist in the far reaches of the universe. Our knowledge of the universe, as time passes, will increase and man's first tentative probes into space in this century will undoubtedly provide scientists and astronomers with even more information to continue their explorations.

Without doubt, astronomy is one of the oldest of the sciences. Men have always been fascinated by the secrets of the sky. Yet even today the possibilities of new discoveries in the field of astronomy are far from exhausted. There are many complex, and undiscovered astronomical phenomena. These will all lead to a greater understanding of man's place in the universe. The Frenchman Jean Perring summoned up, in a few words, just how important the study of the sky is for men: 'It is indeed a feeble light that reaches us from the starry sky. But what would human thought have achieved if we could not see the stars . . .?'

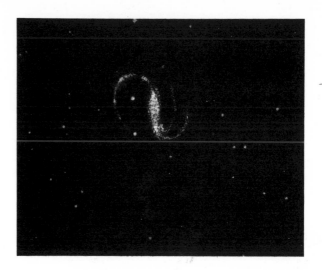

When a remote galaxy shines in the field of the telescope, its light was emitted millions and millions of years ago. At that time man did not exist on the Earth, and the landscapes of our planet looked very different from those of today.

Top: *A barred spiral galaxy.*

Bottom: *A Miocene landscape (from about 40 million years ago).*

159

The book De revolutionibus orbium coelestium *open at the page on which Niccolo Koppernigk (Copernicus's real name) traced his revolutionary scheme for the Solar System. This initiated a vast astronomical movement, which has, as a result of many scholars in many parts of the world, rapidly carried man's knowledge to the threshold of infinity.*

Appendix

ASTRONAUTICS

About 1,800 years ago, the Greek writer Lucian (*c.* A.D. 120–190) of Samosata on the Euphrates River described the first imaginary journey to the Moon. He told the story of a ship on which he found himself, which was blown beyond the Pillars of Hercules by a hurricane of extraordinary violence. The ship rose into the air and would not descend to the sea. The wind filled the sails and for seven days and seven nights the vessel travelled rapidly much higher than the clouds, leaving below it the unexplored expanse of the Atlantic Ocean. 'On the eighth day,' Lucian wrote, 'we saw a great earth, spherical and shining brightly. Approaching it, and disembarking, we landed, and looking at the countryside we found it inhabited and cultivated.'

That fantasy voyage of long ago is being replaced by reality today. The great thrust of the largest rockets which have already been constructed do not take long to propel the space ships which are directed towards the Moon and beyond. The bizarre stories of imaginative artists, indicate how old man's aspirations to travel towards other worlds are.

The journey to the Moon by Lucian is the first narrative about 'journeys in space'. Legends of ascensions to the mysterious celestial spheres are even older. The Greek myth of Icarus, who had been provided with wings thanks to the skill of his father Daedalus and then rose towards the blazing sun until the heat detached his wings which were fixed with glue, is very old. Stranger stories have been handed down from the ancient East. Sanskrit texts from India recount tales of great flying vessels, armed with extraordinary weapons and propelled through the sky by blazing jets. All these legends and stories anticipated future space ships.

In times past, great poets have been fascinated by the stars. Dante described the universe as it was imagined in the Ptolemaic system and it gave him a marvellous frame for his *Divine Comedy* which included much of the knowledge of mediaeval astronomy.

Opposite page: *An astronaut in a test space suit during an earth-bound experiment.*

Below: *Two types of rocket: on the left the rocket is powered with liquid fuel, on the right with solid fuel.*

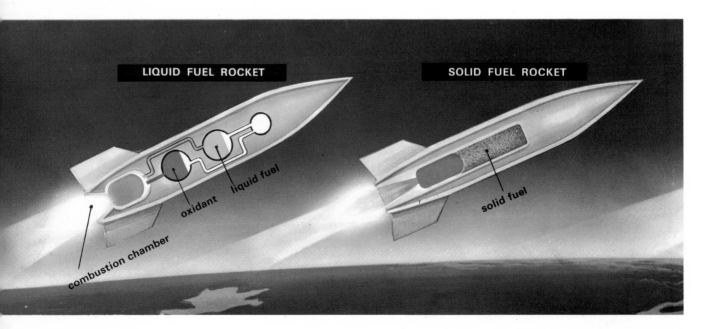

LIQUID FUEL ROCKET   SOLID FUEL ROCKET

liquid fuel

oxidant

solid fuel

combustion chamber

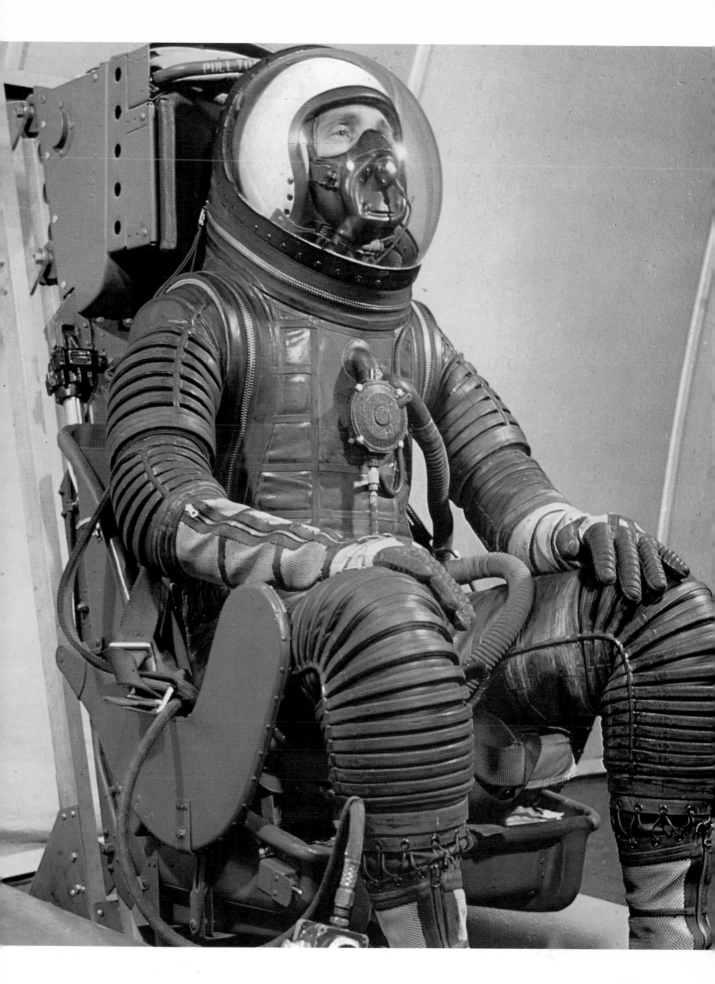

Later, Ariosto told the tale of Astolfo who climbed on the Moon to search for the wisdom of Orlando. These works were, of course, pure fantasy. In those times, the stars were beyond all means of human inquiry. With the invention of the telescope a new era in knowledge enabled man, without moving away from the Earth, to explore the boundless universe populated with gigantic galaxies.

In the very early part of the sixteenth century the Italians Girolamo Fracastoro and G. B. Dalla Porta presented theoretical information on instruments which were later called telescopes. Later in the same century, the skill of making reading spectacles was particularly advanced in Holland. The Dutch lens makers discovered a combination which enabled one to see distant objects more closely and which was the forerunner of the telescope. Nevertheless, these discoveries had no significance for astronomy until Galileo heard of this instrument, and set about making one which he turned to the stars. Suddenly, man possessed a means of

Above left: *The American scientist Robert Goddard with an experimental rocket (1926).*

Above right: Sputnik I, *a Russian spacecraft, the first artificial satellite put into orbit around the Earth.*

Below: *Another Russian artificial satellite* Sputnik III *which has orbited our planet.*

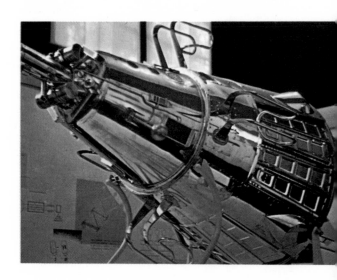

approaching remote worlds and of studying their structure.

Galileo's telescopes were modest. The first one he made only magnified an object ten times and the most powerful only thirty times. However, the cosmos opened before his eyes and those who followed him in the use of this new instrument. Sixty years after the construction of the first astronomical telescope, Newton constructed the first reflecting telescope, substituting a mirror for the objective lens. From the first 'Newtonian' telescope the colossus of Mount Palomar and the radio telescope of Jodrell Bank are descended. The Mount Palomar telescope has a range of thousands of millions of light-years. The optics of the seventeenth century thus quietly foreshadowed the enormous modern instruments which have widened our knowledge of a universe of incredible proportions.

When powerful astronomical telescopes are turned towards the Moon—the celestial body closest to Earth—our satellite seems near enough to touch. The Moon's shadowed craters, the crevasses in its rocks, and the edges of its lava, flow before our eyes as if we were flying over it in a space ship. But this is not enough for the spirit of adventure which animates man. There is a desire to reach these remote bodies in space; perhaps the same spirit which provoked men to climb Mt Everest, which had already been photographed from the air, is an innate need which forms part of human nature. Therefore, it is not surprising that after the invention of the telescope, imaginary journeys to other worlds increased rather than diminished. After these imaginary flights came the real astronauts who have now made the first extra-terrestrial journeys and who are venturing into space with increasing frequency.

In 1649 the Frenchman Cyrano de Bergerac (1620–1655) wrote a bizarre tale entitled *States and Empires on the Moon*. Numerous maps of the Moon had already been drawn using the telescope and there was in existence an atlas of the satellite, the celebrated *Selenographia* drawn and engraved in Danzig by Johan Oevel in 1647. But Cyrano did not take account of this. The means he devised to travel to the Moon were rather curious; among these was a belt of phials full of dew, which, evaporating in the first rays of the Sun, would drag the fanciful astronaut upwards. Cyrano suggested one machine in particular, which was later to be very seriously considered; that is, a complex of rockets. The idea of the means whereby we can travel to other worlds was born in the mind of a writer.

The first tale of a journey to the Moon, conceived in a form based on scientific knowledge, was written only a century ago. This is the romance *De la terre à la lune (From the Earth to the Moon*–1865), by the French novelist Jules Verne (1828–1905), in which the protagonists journey towards the Moon in an aluminium projectile fired from an enormous cannon fixed to the ground in Florida, which gives sufficient thrust to prevent the projectile from falling back to the Earth. In reality this type of launching would result in an instantaneous disaster because of the extremely violent acceleration necessary. The initial thrust would destroy the passengers, and the projectile itself would become red hot as a result of friction with the atmosphere and would evaporate in the end.

Jules Verne tried to present the problem of interplanetary travel factually and he removed it from the field of imagination and dreams. The critics of his impossible cannon ended up by indicating the theoretical bases of the great problem of space travel. They demonstrated the necessity of launching a space craft with a low initial velocity, using a machine capable of moving itself outside the atmosphere. They directed attention towards the only vehicle which can have all these requisites: the rocket.

A rocket is simply a tube, open at its lower end, in which a fuel burns rapidly, producing large quantities of gas which are expelled at the open end. At the open end the gas exercises no effect and expands freely; but in the forward part of the combustion chamber it presses against the internal walls of the rocket and pushes it forward. The greater the speed with which the gas expands the greater the velocity of the rocket. In this propulsion mechanism the presence of an atmosphere has no importance; therefore, it is sufficient that the rocket carries the

On the preceding pages: *A fine photograph of particles which accompanied the flight of the capsule* Aurora 7. *The American astronaut M. Scott Carpenter took numerous pictures in the hope that they would be useful in explaining the mysterious phenomenon, but even now, not one of the many explanations furnished by the experts have thrown much light on the nature of these bodies, even their dimensions are still under discussion.*

Above: *The launching of the American space capsule* Mercury *with the American astronaut John Glenn on board, using an Atlas rocket; 20th of February 1962.*

Opposite page: *The first stage of the gigantic rocket* Saturn *looking at the ends of the rocket motors. Using a rocket of this type, men have circled the Moon.*

necessary oxygen to burn the fuel, and the way to the emptiness of space is open before it.

A Russian, Konstantin K. E. Tsiolkovsky, was the first to study these fabulous possibilities, at the end of the last century. In 1903 he published a carefully calculated work dealing with space ships. Thus, a little less than forty years after the science fiction of Jules Verne, true astronautics was born, even if it was only pure theory and still in an embryonic state. The ideas developed by Tsiolkovsky remain surprisingly modern. He proposed the use of liquid fuels in place of solid ones, because they produce more energy: he foretold the use of multiple stage rockets: and he studied the cabin arrangements for the astronauts which are used today. Self-taught and practically isolated in his work, Tsiolkovsky was limited to theoretical elaborations.

More fortunate was the second of the great rocket pioneers, the American Robert Goddard, who obtained financial support which enabled him to perform practical experiments. In 1926 he was able to launch the first liquid-fuel rocket. In this way early astronautics passed from the theoretical to the experimental stage.

After Goddard's launchings other famous pioneers, like Robert Esnault-Pelterie in France and Hermann Oberth in Germany, studied the problem of space flight more thoroughly and created ever more detailed projects. Finally, before World War II, the German scientist Werner von Braun pioneered in rocketry. Perhaps he was most convinced of the possibility that man could rapidly conquer space. The war blocked his studies and turned them to warlike ends; but from the production of destructive war weapons the first pre-cosmic rocket, the famous V-1, was born—it was the forerunner of all modern missiles.

The V-2 rocket was an intermediate stage between Goddard's small rockets and future space ships and represented a decisive step for the science of astronautics. Von Braun's rocket experiments realised the beginnings of space travel which the pioneers had struggled towards. In the years after the war the V-2 was equipped with scientific

instruments and used to explore the upper atmosphere. In February 1949, a smaller rocket, a Wac Corporal, was attached to a V-2. The complex two-stage rocket was launched, and at a height of 32 kilometres (20 miles) the Wac Corporal was separated and with its propulsion unit in action it reached a height of 402 kilometres (approx. 250 miles) never attained before. The multi-stage rocket was a reality and what Tsiolkovsky had predicted began to become true.

Since then, in a little less than twenty years, progress has been incredibly swift. In the not very distant future we know that extraordinary flights into ever more remote space will take place. When, on the 4th of October 1957, the Russians succeeded in putting the first artificial satellite, *Sputnik I,* into orbit, the world was stupified. But what does this small capsule represent now when compared with the prodigious space probes which explore the Solar System? Yet only a few years have passed: in an extremely short time many difficult problems have been

solved and man has rapidly approached the threshold of human exploration of neighbouring planets. During this period man has learned to navigate in the emptiness of space. But also, man has learned something which the pioneers did not foresee: the exploration of the planets has begun using machines which are controlled remotely by man but not physically piloted by a human.

For the second time in the story of astronomy an unexpected turn has occurred. In 1609 Galileo's telescope opened the way to the study of the stars. Exactly three hundred and fifty years later, the first space probe reached the Moon and opened a new phase in astronomy where instruments are carried near to the planets or even on to their surfaces. The pioneers of astronautics turned their studies solely to the space ship carrying men; they did not conceive of the possibility of receiving and transmitting signals between Earth and space vehicles navigating in remote space.

Space probes are derived from the first

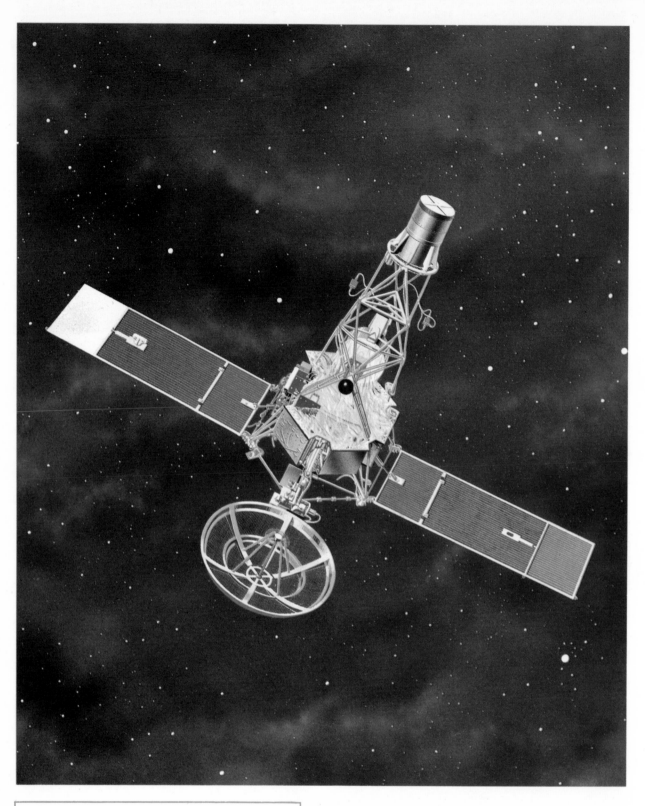

Mariner II *during its flight towards Venus. It was launched in the summer of 1962 and after six months it passed within 35,000 kilometres (21,700 miles) of the mysterious planet perennially covered in clouds.*

artificial satellites and have been rapidly perfected. The problem of the satellites consists of lifting a body above the dense layers of the atmosphere (to avoid the braking effect that these produce, which would immediately deform the satellite's orbit) and giving it such a velocity as to put it in a balanced position like that which maintains the natural satellites in orbit around the planets and the planets around the Sun.

When discussing universal gravitation we examined the principal features of this dynamic equilibrium. The problem of interplanetary probes is only a particular case of the problem of orbiting satellites, because the probe must be freed from the Earth's gravity and placed in a particular orbit; always based, however, on the laws of Kepler and Newton.

The Moon was grazed by the Russian probe *Lunik I* on the 2nd of January 1959 and hit by *Lunik II* on the 12th of September 1959. On the 4th of October of the same year, *Lunik III* revealed dark expanses of lava and great craters shining in the Sun disposed on the Moon's hemisphere which is perpetually invisible from the Earth. The reaction of astronomers throughout the world was one of great excitement. It is true to say that the space era in which we now live started then. The American *Ranger* probes in 1964–65 realised in a short time more progress in our knowledge of the Moon than was obtained over more than three centuries. But the Russian probes in the *Lunik* series and the American *Surveyor* probes of 1966–67 reached still further, landing gently on the bare surface of our satellite, revealing the structure of its smallest pebbles.

In April 1967 *Surveyor III*, using a small shovel, made the first examination of the consistency of the lunar soil, which large orbiting probes had explored in specially selected areas, to ascertain the possibility of landing real space ships.

After the failure of *Surveyor IV* on the night of the 10th of September 1967, *Surveyor V* landed softly on the lunar surface in the eastern part of the Sea of Tranquillity (Mare Tranquillitatis). Apart from the experiments already carried out by *Surveyor III*, *Surveyor V* made an electro-chemical analysis of the lunar surface materials.

Gradually, almost without our noticing it, the Moon has descended from its ancient mythical pedestal and its real features have become familiar. In the meantime, other space vehicles have been launched and they have sent back to Earth new and unexpected information on the worlds which accompany our planet around the Sun.

In 1961 the Russian probe *Venus I* passed within 100,000 kilometres (62,100 miles) of the planet Venus. In 1962 the American *Mariner II* passed at a distance of only 35,000 kilometres (21,750 miles) and transmitted precious information. Three years later *Mariner IV* passed over Mars on the 14th of July 1965 within 16,750 kilometres (10,416 miles) of its surface; the unexpected image of the craters on the red planet were thus revealed to our eyes. A short time later, on the 1st of March, 1966, the Russian *Venus III* sank into the shining clouds of Venus; its shattered structure plunged on to the burning desolate surface of a world which is strange to us and completely outside the Earth-Moon system, which up to a few years before, seemed the only possible place for human exploration.

The extraordinary competition in discovery of the Solar System has just begun. On the 12th of June 1967, another Russian probe was launched towards Venus, *Venus IV*; and in the same week on the 14th of June the American *Mariner V* was launched from Cape Kennedy, Florida, on the same journey. Scientists are now preparing probes designed for 'soft' landing on other planets, similar to those already used for such landings on the Moon. Much longer journeys are being prepared for the exploration of the very remote worlds. It is certain that, in the next few years, new knowledge of the planets will increase and replace the ideas which we have today.

In the wake of the unmanned space probes, advanced patrols of astronauts are waiting to fly towards other worlds. As a result of years of study and experiment, the delicate human machine is now able to survive in space capsules. The problem of variations in gravity which compresses the astronaut in his cabin during launching and leaves him later weightless when the space capsule is in orbit was faced first with animals, almost as soon as artificial satellites were introduced. The relation of weight to gravity was a grave problem and was finally resolved by varying the rates of acceleration and deceleration of the capsule and with special training exer-

171

cises for the astronauts. Meanwhile, technology has produced space ships and other equipment which protects men in space.

On the 12th of April 1961 the Russian Yuri Gagarin started the series of space flights around the Earth which have been made by numerous Russian and American astronauts.

In December 1968 a significant event occurred in man's attempt to fly to other celestial bodies. Three *Apollo* astronauts, Colonel Frank Borman, Captain James Lovell, and Major William A. Anders flew to the Moon, orbited it ten times and returned to splash down safely in the Pacific after a flawless mission. The enormous three stage rocket *Saturn V* put the space vehicle into orbit around the Moon in less than three days. During the flight, which was a triumph of technology, millions of people on Earth watched on television the astronauts' activities in the capsule. Many pictures were taken during the flight, both of the Earth and the Moon, and scientific observations of the Moon were made for the landing of Men.

The launching base of the *Saturn* rocket at Cape Kennedy was appropriately nicknamed the 'Moon Port'. Not far from this locality Jules Verne envisaged his great lunar cannon sunk in the ground; thus it appears that Verne's writings were a prophetic coincidence.

Both the U.S.S.R and the U.S.A. are forging ahead with their space programmes. The manned Russian *Soyuz* and American *Apollo* flights have provided invaluable data and experience for both scientists and astronauts.

The technology of astronautics has just begun and we now look to the future. Since men first orbited the Earth in their space capsules they have shown that exploration of the cosmos is possible and not precluded as men had thought for thousands of years before the twentieth century.

The space capsule Gemini 7 *in flight in space, taken from* Gemini 6 *(December 1965). In the capsule* Gemini 7 *were the American astronauts Frank Borman and James A. Lovell.*

CONCLUSION

In this account we have traced the development of man's ideas about the universe, and we have seen that astronomy has made enormous progress in the last half century. We can now ask, 'What is the future of astronomy?' In reply to this question, we can only base our speculation on recent history which suggests that technological development will continue together with new discoveries and new theories. However, we should be cautious here because some of the most important advances in human thought have not come about through massive technology, but rather through the discoveries and work of clear thinking, often comparatively isolated individuals like Albert Einstein, Max Planck and Lord Rutherford.

There have been periods throughout history of rapid growth in ideas and technology, and we are living through such a time. These are followed by times of stagnation, or even retrogression, such as the Middle Ages. However, the pace of development during the last half century and its continuing acceleration make us believe that unless there are unknown social, political or financial factors which could break this trend, development will continue. This means that there will be some clarification of the problems, such as the origin of the universe, which we recognise today.

The construction of new optical telescopes, such as the giant 240 inch (6 metres) reflector which is being erected in the northern Caucasus, and the proposed telescopes for Arabia and Australia, together with new radio telescopes in various parts of the world and improvements of existing facilities, should provide major advances in our knowledge of the universe. Not only Earth-bound installations, but also remote controlled space-mounted telescopes, either orbiting the Earth or mounted on the Moon, should result in spectacular advances.

There may be a move to reduce the emphasis on man in space and concentrate more on instrumentation. Serious doubts have been expressed by many about the possibility of man escaping from the Solar System, and suggestions have been made that the emphasis in the future should be placed on communications, optical, infra-red and radar astronomy. Whatever the outcome, it will probably be far into the future before man pushes much beyond the Earth-Moon system or our neighbouring planets.

During the next decades we should see instrumented probes investigating the Solar System from Mercury to the giant planets, and plans are advanced for close examination of comets, such as Halley's which is due to appear in 1986.

We are living through a period of intense technological activity and we tend to forget that the basic philosophical and theoretical problems connected with the universe remain to be solved. We may never solve them, but we can be sure that astronomers will continue to search, with constantly improved techniques and instruments, for a satisfactory understanding of the apparently limitless universe.

INDEX

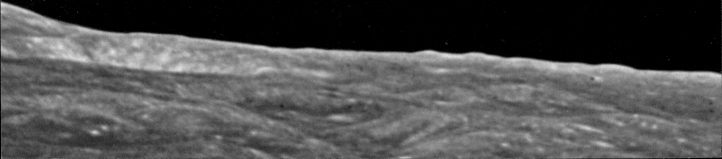